Mr. Tog

Maid of all Work

Wallace Irwin

Alpha Editions

This edition published in 2023

ISBN : 9789357955232

Design and Setting By
Alpha Editions
www.alphaedis.com
Email - info@alphaedis.com

Contents

I
THE HON. VACUUM WHO CLEANS THINGS

I THE HON. VACUUM WHO CLEANS THINGS

To Editor Woman's Page who make bright talk on dusty subjects.

Dear Sir:

I have just abandoned the home of Mrs. Hirem B. Bellus, Trenton, N. J., where I was. I shall describe circumstances, showing how I quit it.

This Mrs. Bellus, 211 lbs. sweethearted lady complete with curly-puff hair, employ me for do Gen. Housework, price $4.50 weekly payment. This are too less money, but she tell me small pay for small Japanese are entirely satisfactory. Satisfactory to who? I ask it. No reply from her.

"Are you an intelligent duster?" are first question for her.

"Japanese dusters is more intellectual than Turkey dusters," I snop back. "I am acquainted with the habits of dirt and how to kill him. I am an experienced soaper and a fearless rubb. Therefore, you hire me."

"Have you ever cleaned with a Vacuum?" she ask to know.

My soul was exhausted to answer this peculiarity.

"I never met him," I acknowledge.

"How could I hire servant girl not familiar with this form of art?" she require peevly. "Vacuum cleaning are most delightful sport of home life to-day. It are enjoyed even in the farthest suburbs of the Universe, and yet you ignore it!"

"Ah, Mrs. Boss Lady," I pledge with pathos, "do not fire me before hiring takes place! Try my sagacity. I shall learn to wrastle with this Vacuum you told about until you are proud to know me."

So she took me to store room and introduce me to Hon. Vacuum.

The Hon. Vacuum that cleans, Mr. Editor, are like an ingrowing garden hose. He can inhale forever without coughing outwards. He are a species of mechanical snake whose breath always travels toward his tail. To use him, following directions must be did:

1—Screw tail of Hon. Vacuum to sprocket in wall.

2—Button the electricity and see what happen.

3—You will hear a sound. It will resemble moan of puppy cats aggravated by Winter blowing cyclones among ghosts. I cannot hear that Vacuum noise without feeling of lonesome poetry.

4—Hon. Vacuum begin to act disturbed. That are sign he want to eat dust.

5—Find some dust. Lead Hon. Vacuum to this and say, "Sick him!" Snorts! Hon. Dust will jump to nowhere while Hon. Vacuum howell for more food.

What are this Hon. Vacuum, anyhows? Hon. Dictionary Book say "Vacuum are Nothing." How could Mr. Danl Webster speak such untruth by his Dictionary? Vacuum cannot be Nothing and yet make so much noises.

This intellectual Vacuum machinery resemble ostriches in what they eat. He delight to sip up tacks, needles, buttons and other hard groceries. He appreciate small wad of paper occasionally, but when I attempt feed him entire newspaper he hold it firmly against his nose, but refuse to go furthermore. I should like a photo of his digestion.

Mrs. Bellus, who are a wonderfully housekept lady, admire this Vacuum more than any of her relatives.

"I hate Dust," she proclaim to me.

"Why should it?" I require. "Nearly all Earth are composed of this delicious powder. Mexico, Sahara Desert & Jersey City is built on dust and enjoys it continuously. Entire Italian army fight to get Tripoli, which are nothing but dust inhabited by Mohammed."

"They are welcome to get it," she snib. "With a regiment of Vacuum Cleaners led by Gen. Housekeeping I could wipe both armies off from Morocco and make it fit to sleep in."

I am shocked by her cleanliness. Yet I ask to know one question.

"Mrs. Madam," I reproach, "tell me this reply. When Hon. Vacuum supp up dust from this carpet, to where do it go to?"

She indicate Heaven with her thumb.

"Up there is grand blow-away hole which shoo it off," she answer it.

So I continue on absorbing hairpins, string and other germs through that succulent machinery.

No lady I work for are equally balanced in their manias. Some are crazed about houseflies; cookery seem to make others continuously het-up; others seem to reverberate with pain when mentioning clothes-starch. This Mrs. Hirem B. Bellus was especially hobbed on that Vacuum Cleanliness. She could forgive all other crimes, no matter if I brought in beefstake too much charcoaled around edges. It no matter if I too sluggish with my feet to answer door when it bells. It no matter if I make outrageous beds or knock gentle glasswear in hard sink. She forgive. But she was deliciously disgusted if Hon. Vacuum was not mourning & howelling all day long while Togo poke its nose around among rugs & other brick-brack.

Her husband disagree from this.

"Togo's biscuits fill my teeth with hatred while his coffee show contemptible weakness," Hon. Bellus dib for breakfast.

"Perhapsly," refute Hon. Mrs., "yet he are one of the best Vacuum Engineers I ever hired."

"I cannot eat a Vacuum," reject that Husband-man, with hat-in-the-ring expression.

"I are not responsible for your animal hungers," corrode this Wife while she arose and gently order me to take Hon. Vacuum down cellar for vacate 2 coal-bins and a ashbarrel.

I retained this situation of jobs for six complete days' work. All day long I go around house dragging hose like a fireman. I got that intelligent Vacuum so trained that he could do tricks of extreme cuteness. He could coax shoe-buttons entirely across room by his talented suction, and when they got up to his nose—gubble! They disappear to zero. He loved to catch flies by breathing them inwards; and once he attempt to withdraw Mrs. Bellus' weak canary bird from cage. Which he not quite did, but too nearly.

So I continue on practicing this suctionary job; and I got so smart from it that I was preparing to request Hon. Mrs. for more wage of salary, when some unpleasantness exploded. I sorry to tell you.

Last Tuesday Hon. Mrs. Hirem B. Bellus come to me and say with gloves & hat:

"I go for lunching at Aunt Maria Stewart whose great wealth includes asthma and make her disagreeable but necessary. Be faithful with your Vacuum while I are away."

I promus her.

"Grocer man will be here this p. m. for collect bill," she corrode with indignation peculiar to debts. "Here are 20$ banknote for payment. I owe him 26$. Tell him to keep the change."

So she part off, leaving me that 20$ paper of extreme value. Mr. Editor, it make me nervus to be alone with great wealth. Sipposing some burglary should come by window? Sipposing my dishonest instinct should fly up and make me skip Canada with cash-money?

Yet I was entirely faithful by that 20$. I took him and fold him to smallish wad, then I lay him carefully in crack of sofa where burglars could not see, yet I could not forget where was. Hon. Vacuum stood near purring softly while I done this. Who could expect what shall be?

Me & Hon. Vacuum continue our vacuous task, making kick-back of dust wherever was. I run him over rugs so oftenly that he pull holes from them. I make him sniff all cobble-webs from the pictures & poke his nose into each corner where was. We was very friendly, me & Vacuum.

I continue to vac. After Hon. Vacuum had sniffed off all wall paper, sideboard, etc., I remember how upholsterish chairs & sofas must be cured of germs also, so I vacuate these velvet upholsters. I was doing very nicely, thank you, when, of suddenly, I point nose of Hon. Vacuum to sofa where that 20$ bill was setting tightly. Yet no financial panics came to me until—O FRIGHTS!! *That 20$ bill begin hopping toward Hon. Vacuum's nose with hypnofied expression peculiar to birds when eaten by charming snakes!*

I make snatch for money— alast! I was too late in beginning. Hon. Bill make leap to nose of Hon. Vacuum—gollup! Down long, thin throat of this machinery that wealthy cash was swallowed. I try to choke him so he give it back,—but useless it was. That cash-paper had flipped into his interior digestion before Jack Robinson could say it.

So I unbotton electricity and look down Hon. Vacuum with considerable angry rage. What had he did with my trustful money? O how my indignation jump up! How could this mechanical snake treat me so trickful after I had chaperoned him and fed him dust for several complete days? I shook him with grand cruelty in hopes to make him cough back that wealth of Mrs. Hirem B. Bellus. He remain entirely bulldoggish with that bill clasped somewheres inside.

Then I remember how Mrs. Bellus had told me how trash suctioned away by Hon. Vacuum was blowed high-ward through hole in roof. Maybe I should catch that 20$ yet before he got out! So with immediate quickness I got top-ladder & clomb to roof where I dishcover hole. Yet it was entirely penniless. Now & occasionally slight spurt of dust blow from hole; sometimes one shoe-button would popp out from where Hon. Vacuum had kicked him. Yet that hole remain like a bursted bank, refusing to surrender money.

Afar off in direction of Pennsylvania I could observe slight dusty expression of sky. I feel sure that was Mrs. Bellus' money travelling West.

Enjoying great discouragements I got down from that roofly seat and wrote following telegram to Mrs. Bellus before walking farewell:

> "Togo is resigned. Hon. Vacuum blow your 20$. So sorry to say. The unexpected often happen, so you may get this money back, as I do not see how you ever can. When last seen it was going to Pennsylvania where I shall be there to catch it if he fall down and send back by P. O. delivery."

When I wrote this telegram I pin him to kitchen door and walk rapidly away with expression of one going West and expecting to arrive there. And while travelling I think of one wise quotation: "Nature abhors a Vacuum." I am agreeable to Nature in this.

Hoping you are the same,
Yours truly,
Hashimura Togo.

II
HON. BABY AND WHAT TO DO WITH HIM

II HON. BABY AND WHAT TO DO WITH HIM

To Editor Woman's Page, who was once a Baby, but has got over it.

Dear Mr. Sir:

I have now released myself from Patriot's Bluff, Ohio, where I took considerable experience away with me. There I done home-work for Mr & Mrs Henery M. Bushel & child for delicious cheapness of wages, thank you. When I approach this Bushel home 2 weeks formerly from now, Hon. Mrs (refined lady with wealthy golden tooth) look severely at my Japanese humility.

"Togo," she narrate, "this house contains the brightest, most valuable & booflest Hon. Baby in all world."

I attempt to look surprised. "Mrs Madam," I say gradually, "I have worked already at 13½ places which also contained the brightest, most valuable & booflest Hon. Baby in all world. How could it? Did them other places all have same baby?"

"No. But them other babies was all imposters," she dib.

So she led me to setting-room, walking with quiet toes and wrapped expression peculiar to folks approaching Mikado or some other President. In 1/8 size rocking-bed I observe Hon. Baby laying among considerable softness and appearing quite babyhood.

"Are he not remarkabilious child?" she require.

"I are sure he must be very distinguished," I say sweetishly.

"Why you think so?" she require with gently smiling.

"Because," I says so, "all distinguished persons appears quite plain when first observed."

"I do not care to hear your foreign thoughts," she grudge.

Hon. Baby make happy guggle to see me, so I know we should get very friendship together. I waggle my thumbs to him, so he make more laugh.

"DON'T!!" holla Hon. Mrs. "You wish explode my child's nerves by this actions?"

"Are it injurious for childhood to laugh at my thumbs?" I ask it.

"Many children are spoilt forever by too much laughter in infancy," she explan. "I raise this child like I raise biscuits—by book. Volume entitled 'How Do It to Grow Best Children' tell me delicious nervus diseases what children will be entitled to if not careful. By feeding, exercise, etc., I intend to make this Babe great man for future."

"Shall he be Presidential Candidate, perhapsly?" I require.

"No! he shall never have such brutal treatment!" she exclam. "Yet I are sure he shall be great because he has his grandfather's eyes."

I could not believe such youngly child could rob old gentleman of his eyesight. Yet I say nothing. "Have he got a name?" I require for chivalry.

"Several," she report. "He are pronounced Alexander Applegate Leopold Bushel."

"Bushel baskets have been filled with less," I say punnishly. "That name surrounds him completely."

"For shortness we call him Goo," she say so. "Now I shall tell you his daily programme." She take paper from table and read me following list of deeds intended for that Babyhood:

5:30 to 6 A. M. crying exercises enjoyed for development of lung.

6:15 sterilised milk programme with bottle.

7:30 Hon. Baby bathed in fluid offensive to mikrobes. Hon. Father then permitted to bring out scales and weigh Hon. Baby so to show he soon will be a Physical Perfection like Family.

8:10 A. M. ½ hour baby-talk conversation by his mother for development of brain.

8:40 slight perambulation in baby-cab continuing 2 hours. This trip must go through considerable streets and scenery, so Hon. Baby will get used to travel.

10:40 homeward arrival. More crying exercises enjoyed for benefit of lung.

11:30 continual sleep programme until entirely saturated with slumber.

Afternoon—same like morning programme, only more so.

Hon. Mrs Bushel told me this with intense accuracy peculiar to statistics.

"You speak reverently about sterilised milk," I pronounce. "How do you make this youthful beveridge?"

"This milk are best science for all baby," she report. "You put him in clean kettle & boil him to scalding point—"

"Boil Baby to scalding point?" I screech with shocks.

"No!! Boil milk," she otter.

Which show what difficult housekeeping babies can be.

*   *   *

Mr Editor, one important rule I notice about babies—you must not never give them nothing that they want. This Hon. Bushel Baby are continuously poking forth sweet hands and making considerable blueness from his eyes to show his undesirable whims & requisitions. One time I was approaching steps with 100-lb ice-chunk for kitchen. Hon. Baby seen this and order some by making finger-signals. How could I disobey this toy boss? So I split off slight fracture of ice & was attempting to make present of this to him when— O scream! Mrs Boss came flewing outward and seen what was.

"Stop!" she holla. "You wish refrigerate that darling interior?"

I feel entirely hashed for my ignorance.

Another occasion Hon. Baby reach forth and begin eating loose end of my pink calicoed apron with toothless expression of sublime joyness. While he ate he say, "Ah-Goo!" which are Chinese words meaning "a good salad can be made of almost anything."

Screams!!! "What style murder are you serving to my child now?" yall Mrs Henery M. Bushel hysterically.

"Excuse please. Are aprons injurious for food supply?" I ask to know.

For answer Hon. Mrs Bushel grabb him to arms & rosh at telephone.

"Hello, Doctor yes, come to the poisoning quick!" she gollup. Then she walk forward & back adding groans while Hon. Baby observe her emotions with great amusement.

Honk-honk to door. Hon. Dr Ottomobile arrive with chuggs & he hop forthly containing bags and implements.

"Where is poison?" he require, calm but nervus while his beard look entirely scientific.

"Here are!" hissy Hon. Mrs tearing forth my apron. "Hon. Baby ate this heartily."

Hon. Dr took out mikeroscope. First he look at Hon. Baby through his mouth, then he poke that glass against my apron and peep with earnestness.

"This article contain 101 per cent. venomous products," he explan. "In addition there is maniac acid solution with hypocritical sublimate. I am surprised to see your child looking so well, because by Science he should be dead 9 times."

Hon. Mrs wept, but Hon. Baby continue making gurgle-laugh with Xmas dinner expression. For 48 complete hours his parents continued standing on end, expecting that child to perish off, because he was so much better behaved than usual.

*　　*　　*

Me & Alexander continue to be dear college chums; yet I was entirely nervus to approach him, because I was afraid I might explode some science connected with it. But all commencements have their finish. One day it came thusly:

"Take Hon. Baby for sidewalk promenade," holla Mrs Henery M. Bushel from upstairs side. "You will find peramble-buggy on front porch. You must begone 2 hours and not aggrevate him by your foolish attentions. If he begin to cry, wheel homewards."

"Shall do so," I terminate.

"And remember thus," she commute. "So long as he silent, you must not notice him."

So I put on hat & go forthly to front porch where peramble-buggy was there. I wheel this along without noticing Hon. Baby, because I was ordered to snub it. The faithful duty I always possess made me entirely noble. I did not even peek in buggy for see how he look. Such were my obedience to commandments. For 1 hour I push that child-cab through fashionable streets where he can become educated by society sights. Silence from him. For 21 minute I wheel him by rivers, trees & scenery where he could become educated in Nature. Silence yet from him. For 15 minute I ride him by bank-buildings, offices, drug-stores, so he can get educated in business conditions. And yet he remain silent like a hypnofied fly. His refined behaviour made me feel lonesome—to pass 1 hour, 36 minute without some cry-exercises were too much for me to believe. He must be wrong somewheres. So, in defy to Hon. Boss Lady's orders, I lift back top from that child-carriage—and O shocks! What I seen? Nothing!! Hon. Baby were not there!!!!!!

My brain began running backwards. Where could Hon. Baby went? Was he pulled out of buggy by airships while I was not looking? Had he drop from bottom of that cart or crolled over side and eloped secretively? I confused in all directions while my heart remained stationary.

With empty baby-trundle I trott along each sidewalk requiring, "You seen loose baby?" from each persons who said they didn't. Hon. Police come and ask me what was. I told so.

"Black Hand stole um!" Holla Hon. Police with rabid calm. So he commence to trott along by me while 48 mobbed persons join up with us. "Have you saw loose baby?" everybody ask it. Nobody had.

Finally, made desperado by my fear, I decide to return back to home of Bushel and report what was. So elope I there, chaperoned by Hon. Police & persons. I stood by porch with quaker knees, knowing Mrs Bushel would be irritated to lose such nice child. While I stood thusly—beholt! Door flew ope and out come Hon. Mrs carrying Hon. Baby in arms!

"Fool Togo!" she yellup.

"Yes, please!" This from me.

"When you left house with Hon. Buggy how could you forgot?"

"Forgot what?" I asked to know.

"You forgot Baby!" she snagger.

Then I remember what was. When I left house she told I shouldn't disturb Hon. Baby, so I forgot to look see if he was there in Hon. Buggy!

"Mrs Madam," I erupt, stretching myself upwards to Samurai height. "By not taking your baby out and losing him, I saved his life. Yet I shall charge you nothing for this heroism."

"You shall save his life again by eloping away from hither at once," she dib wild-cattishly. "Leave baby-cab on front porch and let me see your absence."

So I made very sorry removal feeling similar to one who make a living swallowing dull swords.

Hoping you are the same, Yours truly,
Hashimura Togo.

III
HON. MISS DRESSMAKER

III HON. MISS DRESSMAKER

To Editor Woman's Page Who Understand How Ladies Can Be Dress-Made Until They Appear Beautiful.

Dear Mr Sir:

During my progress around from places to places I have got acquaintance with all sorts American musical instruments. Banjos, gasolene, stoves, trumbones and basso drums I have heard shooting their music. But never until of recently did I encounter a sew-machine doing so. Sew-machines are different from pianos in several ways. Pianos are good for accompany ladies singing; sew-machines are useful for accompany ladies gossiping. This I notice.

Place at which I was most formerly employed was Mrs Jno W. Smith (pronounced the same way) who reside by her husband near Poison Ivy View, Conn.

This Mrs Smith have a mind full of drygoods. She speak of her friends in dressmake language entirely.

"Jno," she say to her husband when they set down for dinner-eat ceremony, "to-day I met the most charming Brussels lace with accordeon tassels at wrists and elbows."

"What was her name in real life?" require Hon. Smith with nervus expression of check-book.

"Mrs Ethel Crabapple," report Hon. Mrs Jno, her mind making drop-stitches of fashionable pattern. "She have took up woman-suffrage movement and speaks very beautiful under her pink majolica hat of baby ostrich plumes."

Hon. Jno Smith sigh like a bye-gone day.

"Ethel Crabapple!" he renig for slight sentiment. "I knew her when she was merely Ethel Scraggs. How is she?"

"Quite well, I think," relapse Mrs Jno. "She spoke on Progress wearing a green opera cloak of cerise burlap aggrevated with panels of Arabian chiffon and satin annex at collar."

Hon. Smith withdraw himself from this conversation for fear he might be asked to buy some similar uniform for his wife.

When this Mrs Smith are asked to ball-parties, dance-step festivals, trolley-ride, bridge-play gambol, etc., she look extremely downtrodden for days & days. Her husband remain calm but frightened, like Wall Street before it collapses. Of finally she lead Hon. Smith to breakfast where she report distinctually,

"I am absent of all clothing to wear anywheres."

I do not notice this. But Hon. Jno grone severely while he give her all the wealth of his pockets. Then he go glubly away to his office feeling like the Queen of Sheba's husband when it was fashionable for ladies to dress in solid gold with diamond buttons.

About one week of yore my Hon. Boss Lady come at me and decry,

"Togo," she say, "one extra plate must arrive to table this week."

"You expecting some person?" I ask out.

"No. Only a dressmake," report her.

"Must I mix extra food for her daily?" I snuggest.

"Ah, no, not to do," she repartee with economy voice. "This Miss Dressmake will eat what the family does."

"If she eat what the family does, what will the family eat?" I ask to know.

No reply to this request.

Several considerable days before Miss Dressmake arrive up, Mrs Jno W. Smith spend many literary hours pursuing stylish magazines full of smiling ladies dressed in colours. Each ladies in them pictures was surrounded by diagrams & patterns showing how she was made. Mrs Smith select these portraits carefully, to see which she would rather look like. She prefer portrait of lady named "Style 41144B." She say she would request Hon. Dressmake to fix her appearance like that.

"How you describe this dress, please?" I ask to know.

"It is a pan velvet shirred and basted with the yoke separated from the white," she report.

"Eggs can be cooked in similar stylish fashion," I communicate. She do not seem to assimilate them words I said.

Day before arrival of Hon. Miss Dressmake this Mrs Smith derange back parlor with delicious variety of cloth to resemble drygoods emporium.

Spools, tapes & other patterns are confused everywheres. You would expect Panama Canals could be built from such a preparations.

"Are dressmake-ladies expensive artists to employ?" I ask it.

"Deliciously so," she pop back. "They cost $1.50 per daily, not to mention wear and tear on food and sew-machine. I expect this lady to make me 2 ball-dance gowns, 1 wrapping-kimono, 1 stylish walk-suit, 2 costumes for afternoon tea ceremony and ½ doz. pajamas for Hon. Jno Smith. She will be employed nearly 4 days."

"How can you possibly make any profit from her?" I ventriloquate. No reply as yet.

Pretty soonly Hon. Annie B. Goblin (Miss), slightly spinster lady of detached age, arrive up to do this dressmake employment. Her complexion was concealed behind freckles. She might of been beautiful, had she not been homely.

This Miss Goblin lady understood international sewing to any extent. She could combine Irish lace, China silk and Persian embroidery on the same dress without the least race-riot. Few politicians can keep so many nationalities together calmly.

She were a very talented sewing-bee who never quit buzzing with conversations. She was one of them ladies what makes newspapers useless.

Last Thursday A. M. Hon. Mrs Smith give her $4.80 worth of Baptist silk and command her to create a dress to resemble Princess Patricia, so much as possible.

"At that price I can make you look like a Queen slightly marked down," communicate Hon. Annie B. Goblin, making whizz with sew-wheel, at same time telling delicious society news with her pincushion voice.

"Mrs Horse W. Harvey hope to be a widow soon," she report between stitches. "She has took up voice culture which must kill her husband with rapidity. She owe me $8.64 for two years and her Jewish lynx set is merely her husband's fur overcoat warmed over."

"I have long enjoyed that delicious suspicion," deploy Mrs Jno W. Smith, who do not care for gossip, but merely stay near to oversea that job.

"Mrs van Swallow Tagg has a mortgage on her house which leaks," continue on this sewing-wasp. "I am sorry for her peevish temper which is a disease. Her husband is a good man, but dishonest."

"She wears her hats unbearably," reproach Mrs Jno W.

"Mrs Cyrus Q. Bogle's prominent Aunt Angelica drinks patent medicine for her rheumatism."

"How shocked I am!" explode Hon. Mrs. "Tell me some more."

"Her nephew Joshua who goes to Yale to study footballing—excuse, please, would you prefer to have this yoke hooked or cut bias?"

"Cut bias, please," exclam Mrs Smith with tense voice. "What did you say about Mrs Bogle's Nephew Joshua who go to Yale?"

"He arrive home from Yale smelling distinctually of cigarettes. He cannot last long."

"Them Bogles contain very common stock," repose Mrs Jno. "I seldom could admire Mrs Bogle's character since she came to church in that flowered dimity with panniers of heliotrope velour cut umpire style at the neck with a demi-train of Belgian brocade."

"I respect your grief," relapse Hon. Annie B.

"Although she are one of my dearest friends," explan Mrs Smith, "I am obliged to add stinginess to her other disagreeable virtues. In despite of the fact that her husband owns one complete livery stable, she still continues to behave like the Middle Classes. Her silk dresses are only nearly."

Jing-jing!! This from front door bell. Too bad I had to answer, because I was fascinated to hear that brutish remark of Hon. Bogles. Howeverly, I was dutiful as usual; so I elope to door-knob. There stood one lady wearing fashionable complexion. She poke forth following print on call-card:

Mrs Cyrus Q. Bogle
At Home When She Is.

"Are Mrs Smith residing here this afternoon?" require Mrs Bogle.

"Yes, if convenient," I say to.

"Are she too busy to appear?"

"Yes. Thanks."

"Will she not appear to me, her dear-friend?"

"No, Mrs Madam. Sorry. Too busy."

"Busy what with?" This from her.

"She are employing a dressmake lady to gossip about you."

"Me!!" she exclam without sugar.

Silence.

"What stitches did this dressmake person take in my character?" she corrode.

"She say your Aunt Angelica drink medicine."

"Truthfully, she does."

"She report your nephew Joshua eat cigarette-smudge."

"I might deny that uselessly."

"She describe your husband's doggish habits."

"I also realise them."

"She explain how your dress contains flounced dimity with spaniels of heliotrope cut umpire-fashion at neck with—"

"No more!" holla Mrs. Bogle dropping fire from her eyebrows. "Such reports are false as they are truthless. I permit neighbours to abuse my family, but when they distort my gowns I draw the string!"

She done so by making door-bang and departing offward amidst furies.

"Togo, who has came and went all at once?" require Hon. Mrs from upstairs.

"Mrs Cy Q. Bogle, please."

"Mrs Bogle—how strange. I was just discussing her."

"I told her you was." This from me.

"WHAT!!!!" This from her.

I repeat. Loud silence. Sew-machine stop, gossip stop, dressmake stop.

"Annie," I hear Mrs Jno W. Smith say, "Bring me glass of water to faint with. Also discharge Togo sooner than possible."

This sound so unwelcome to me that I refuse my situation by going away. So I elope to trolley with suit-case, feeling quite the reverse.

Hoping you are the same
Yours truly
Hashimura Togo.

IV
THE HUSBAND'S PLACE IN THE HOME

IV THE HUSBAND'S PLACE IN THE HOME

To Editor Woman's Page, who give Ladies such delicious advice how to preserve raspberries, beauty and other species of vegetables.

Hon. Mr:

At home of Mrs. Washington Fillups where I was employed as recently as 3 days of yore I obtain many chances to observe some ladies when they call.

One day Mrs. Oliver Hix approach & make ring-ring to front door which I oped to permit her in. I notice she was displayed very stylishly with calling-card appearance. Her goldy hair contained one (1) velvet hat of extreme blackness and her dress was all surrounded with fringes like a piano-cover or like that Indian costume of Hon. Buffalo Bill.

"Are Mrs. Fillups to home?" she inquire pridefully poking forth her name with card.

"She are," I report. "Yet I must go to see if she will acknowledge it."

Hon. Mrs. Fillups were up in sewing-room mending sox with considerable darn. When I told her who was there she report, "Her again?" Then she dust off her nose, reorganise her hairpins and trot downward to where Mrs. Hix was.

Kiss-kiss heard. Joy shreeks. Conversations in soprano duet.

It was my duty to massage off the mahogany furniture in dining-room annexed to parlour, so how could I avoid overhearing what they said? I did not attempt to do so, however much I tried. It was my duty to polish that furniture in dining-room, so there I was. If ladies cannot keep their conversation hushed, Servants cannot make their ears behave. This is human-natural.

After dis-cussing topicks like baby, coal-bills & other luxuries, they commenced gossiping about some articles of furniture I could not understand. Their voices was so interrupted I could not catch-all, but this is what I heard:

Mrs. Hix say: "I permit mine to set in parlour when company comes. This is most ostentatious place."

From this I thought she was talking about a piano.

"I move *mine* into library every night after dinner," revoke Mrs. Fillups. "He are too smoky for parlour."

From that I supposed she was talking about a stove.

"I have had mine for ten continuous years," say Mrs. Hix saddishly, "and from experience I am sure they are all alike. No use to be neat and tidy when they are there. They will not stay put like other furniture. Set them in one place and you will find they have moved somewhere else. Dust seems to collect wherever they stand.

"I have never seen one that could make a baby comfortable. Neither are they able to hold a newspaper without dropping it carelessly here & there," report Mrs. Hix with saddish grone of dispair.

"And yet strange thing," interject Mrs. Fillup. "How useless home would seem if it did not contain one!"

Mrs. Fillup & Mrs. Hix now make whisper with hissy voices. I could not hear, although both my ears stood endwise with excitement. I wish folks would not be so secretive when they have secrets!

Pretty soonly Hon. Hix Lady make up-riseing and depart off. More kiss-kiss ceremony. She go. Then she step back and say more. She go again, but come back for an encore. More conversations containing secretive talk. Ladies is always thus—they tell all the important news in the postscript.

Pretty soonly she was gone entirely. I step forth to Mrs. Fillups.

"Hon. Boss Lady," I say with boldness peculiar to Samurai, "do you not hire me to be as intellectual as possible abut household duties?"

"I do exactly," she otter. "Why do you ask to know?"

"Do you not require that I should know all peculiarities about your furniture?" I ask it.

"Absolutely everything," she outcry.

"All well then," I renig. "There is something I wish to know what. In recent conversation which I overheard accidently while standing at key-hole, I hear you speak about one article of furniture which I am not familiar of. By the way you describe it, it sets in parlour like piano until it begins smoking like a stove; then you move it to library where it holds baby like a cradle and supports newspapers like a table! When you set it anywheres it moves nervusly from room to room, dropping dust like a elephant. It is a failure at everything around the house, yet you say so that no home is complete without one. What kind of a conundrum are you talking about, please?"

"My husband," report Mrs. Fillups as she elope away.

This husband belonging to Mrs. Fillups are quite a large gentleman. I are not sure if husbands comes in regular sizes, but I should think Hon. Fillups was about size 46. It are deliciously difficult to housekeep him.

Mrs. Fillups spend all day-long cleaning up after his departure and preparing for his next visitation. Her favourite pet name for him is "Don't."

When he encroach home by evening train she meets him on door-mat with cheerful smiling. Yet she has got her watch eye open for his uncivilised ways.

"Don't track snow on rug, dearie, Don't wear rubbers in house, DON'T leave them on front steps like a tenement." Hon. Fillups are one of those husbands which begins to obey orders after the damage is done.

"Darling, don't leave it on sofa," she report when he remove off hat & coat. "Don't lay cigars on mahogany table & DON'T whistle in house."

When he make wash-hand ceremony she say, "Don't dry your thumbs on clean towels!"

"What are clean towels for?" he ask saddishly.

"I hang them in bathroom to show company how extravagant we are with our laundry," rejoint Mrs. Fillups. "In this era of hard times towels are not made merely to be used."

Dinner is served. At Hon. Table where they set there she resume conversation. "Don't tip soup plate in eating it," she report cow-cattishly. "Don't stand up while carving mutton. Don't eat salad with oyster fork!"

When dinner is completely finished Hon. Fillups promenade in direction of parlour. His teeeth now contains one enlarged tobacco pipe of sunburned appearance.

"DON'T!!" holla Hon. Mrs. with ghost-voice. "The parlour must be saved from that pipe. I have prepared the library for your comfort where you can set among the books you love and read the newspapers. There you can do what you like and feel homeful."

Hon. Fillups go to library. There he find one tight-back wicker chair setting hopefully beside table. On that chair are laid out one smoke jacket containing velvet collar of charming red. Befront of his chair are two (2) complete slippers of carpet toes. On table are 12 refined cigars of freckled complexion. On table next by this are works of Hon. Robt. Browning bound in one-half calf and containing blue ribbons to mark Mr. Fillups favourite poems, which he has never read.

Hon. Husband make walk-in to this library where he take *Evening Telegram* from his pocket and unfold it on table. Then he go to opposite corner of room, remove off his coat, pick out one large velvet-coloured chair, light Hon. Pipe and commence reading News with expression of intense relief.

"Why don't you put on smoke-jacket what I arrange for your comfort?" requires Mrs. Fillups with injury voice.

"Too hot, dearness," he report from news.

"But it matches the room so nicely," she dib. "When will you learn to be a decoration? Also I give you 12 fashionable cigars for Xmas and you continue making puff-puff with that horid old pipe."

"I would never be so cruel as to burn up your gifts," he repartee. "Besides this pipe, though strong, is more gentle in its strength than many cigars of twice its weakness."

"I fix you nice wicker chair by lamp-shade, yet you continue to spill ash on fine velvet furniture. Why is?"

"Velvet, though expensive, has a way of feeling soft to tired business men," he explain, looking ashamed.

"Also I have fixed works of Hon. Robt Browning for your benefit. Why do you continue to snub this great poet?"

"I mean him no personal injury," say Hon. Fillup. "Unfortunately I can find better murders in newspapers, and they are easier to read."

So he continue through the evening, setting in his cuff-sleeves, smudging his pipe and looking very misfit.

Last Wednesday morning when he was departing off for his office he say with hopes:

"I shall bring college friend Charlie Stringer home for dinner, if convenient."

"Don't!" she say continuously.

"For why?" he ask out.

"Because," she snagger, "Wednesday are Irish stew night, and we are scarce on this economical vegetable. Sifficient for three are less than enough."

"Oh, then!" he report. "Charlie and me shall dine together at the Runabout Club where hasty food can be obtained abundantly day and night."

"Don't!" besearch Mrs. Fillups. Too late for reply.

That evening by late P. M. that dinner plate for Mr. Fillups set lonesome. Mrs. Fillups remain by table weeping into bill-of-fare.

"Why do you weep?" I require at lengthly.

"He will not return home for meals when I do everything for his comfort!" she sub.

"Mrs. Madam, excuse my chivalry, but I must speak a lecture," I say forth. "If you would be less careful of his comfort, maybe he would be more comfortable. Many husbands quit home because it is too beautiful. I realise that they do not know what is best for them. They are cross-eyed in their intelligence. Yet are it not better to permit them to be miserable in their own way, if this makes them happy? You must remember: Husbands should not be furniture for the home—Home should be furniture for the Husband. I speak this because I saw it."

"Elsewhere is best place for such a wise servant!" snib Mrs. Fillups leaping to her feets. So I project myself away feeling quite absorbed like a sponge.

Hoping you are the same,
Yours truly,
Hashimura Togo.

V
HOW SHOULD I DO PAPER-BAG COOKING?

V HOW SHOULD I DO PAPER-BAG COOKING?

To Editor Woman's Page, which makes photographs of food and other amusements.

Dear Sir:

I am a Japanese Schoolboy employed as a servant girl, but I am not doing so this week, thank you. I am such a continual office-seeker around Employment Bureaus that Hon. Boss say, "Back again!" whenever he sees me arriving.

I shall tell you what happened last.

Mrs. S. W. Swingle, gentlemanly lady of red-haired beauty, say tackfully, "I will employ you at great risk. Please arrive to my home to-night."

There I went. This S. W. Swingle lady reside with her husband and children respectively at Railroad View, N. J. Her Mr. Swingle, to which she is married, is a timetable as well as a husband. His soul is full of trains. He arrive home at 6.43 and require dinner at 6.59. He go to bed at 11.04 and demand breakfast at 7.22 so he can catch 8.12 train.

When I got on this job I dishcovered that my tranquillity was going to be very scarce. I must greet milkman at dawn-light and continue my domestic science all day until exhausted.

Mrs. S. W. Swingle, with sweethearted expression, say that busy folks is most happy. If this is truthful I should prefer to be slightly miserable on Sunday and Thursday afternoons.

Yet I remain stationary in employment until Monday when sorrow arrive wrapped up in a Paper Bag. I shall tell you how was.

At hour of 2.44 Mrs. S. W. Swingle arrive to kitchen with cutting expression peculiar to scissors.

"Togo, why for do you prepare such bad food?" she decry with angry rage. "There is no uplift in your biscuits. Your beef is boiled until it lose all originality. Mr. S. W. Swingle, who is far from strong, say your coffee is the same. And so forth. You must learn to discontinue this. If we cannot fare better you must farewell."

My soul feel punctured by this conversation. It seem very brutal for me to go loose again when jobs is so infrequent to obtain.

While thusly I was thinking I find on tip-shelf of pantry one slight brown book. It was wrote by a Kitchen Professor and bore this remarkable title:

"PAPER-BAG COOKING."

This paper-bag food was invented by a French professor, I read. How economical those French can be! I thought. I had oftenly heard how French chef could make stylish meals out of mere remnants. They are famus for deceiving pork till it taste like chicken and giving boiled codfish the same expression as turtle soup. To such genius paper bags is easy problem.

I read this book reverentially. It say for Introduction:

> "Paper bags when cooked properly contain new flavours you never would imagine was there. It is considerable nourishing, as none of its juice escapes. You can learn to cook one by reading Instructions and becoming utterly fearless."

My heart make happy laugh. I shall cook some of these paper bags for that dear Swingle family so they will forgive me for my previous food. So I read this book and learn how do-so. I am incomplete in the American language, but this is how I understand him to say:

> *"How to Cook Paper Bags*
>
> "Select one paper bag which is fresh and tender. Medium-size kind are most delicate, as large-size kind are apt to be tough, especially in the fall. Butter this bag inside and salt tastefully. Use meat or whatever pork chops are in icebox to stuff bag with. Add one vegetable until satisfied. The bag is now ready to roast.
>
> "Next take one oven. Heat it to hotness of about 300 thermometers. Poke Hon. Bag inside this and see what happens. Occasionally make peek into oven to observe how bag behaves. If Hon. Bag catch afire, put out. Do not be discouridged. When he is sufficiently cooked, remove out and chop with shears. Serve hot. You will be surprised to taste it."

I follow this literary directions with faithfulness peculiar to Samurai. First I got one small, young paper bag which formerly contained string beans. I supposed from what I read in that Book that paper bags should be stuffed like turkeys to make nicest roast. So I fill him with following food which I obtain from icebox:

> 1 lbs complete beafstake knifed into small pieces
> ½ bottel tomatoes catch up
> Representative beets, onions, carots and potatus
> Plentiful water moistened to taste

That Swingle kitchen contain one gas-stove of 40 horse-power capacity and includes one oven which is easily het up to angry rage. I light this oven. Great heat arrive. Then I place Hon. Paper Bag carefully in one drip-pan, pour over it some slight water, so it wouldn't burn, and poke inside oven. Then I set down thoughtful and await the future.

Mrs. S. W. Swingle arrive to kitchen with question-mark expression in her blue eye.

"What we shall have for dinner, Togo?" she ask out nervely.

"Ah, Mrs. Madam! If I should tell you, you would cease to be surprised. Yet it is something exalted I shall offer you. So different from those monotonous foods previously experienced!" All this I spoke.

That lady retreat away expectfully.

I watch this cookery by alarm clock to see it shall not be too long. Hon. Book say "When bag are stuffed with meat, cook 25 minute. When stuffed with vegetables, cook 20 minute." I figure this arithmatic with lead-pencil. That bag was stuffed with both meat and vegetables, therefore 20+25=45. That bag must cook 45 complete minutes to be sifficiently delicious.

At end of 14 minutes I take slight peek to oven. O sakes! You would not know Hon. Bag for himself, he was so swole. He contain more uplift than one quart yeast. He was so baloonical in shape that I fear he might float upward containing meat and vegetables. Therefore I prick him slightly with fork.

POPP!!

Grand explode arrive. I am shot by out-rush of stewed steam which jump out amidst delicious flavour. Hon. Bag flop back completely exhausted. No more puff up for him. He droop amidst them meat and vegetables like a wet sail in a shipwreck. I close oven door deceptively. Hon. Book say nothing about this angry behaviour of food. Maybe that will improve its nourishing qualities.

After it had been some time in baking condition I was enabled to enjoy the perfume of this aroma. Each food when it cook make some odor of smell. Apple pie smell like joyful hunger of schooldays. Roast beef smell like powerful appetite of athelete. But paper bag smell like fire among newspapers. I notice this.

While this food was roasting I look out of window and observe Hon. Robert Jackson, near neighbour, approach and make knock to door.

"Mrs. Madam," he report when that Swingle lady come to door, "I announce your house is afire."

"How you know?" requesh she with pale voice.

"Because I smelt burned wall-paper distinctually!"

Loud screem by Mrs. S. W. Swingle. They rosh to cellar. Nothing was burning there—not even the furnace. They trot to roof. Nothing was smoking there—not even the chimbley.

"It must be Uncle Oliver burning autumn leaves," explan Hon. Jackson. How could he know it was my cooking he smelt?

When nextly I peek into oven I observe Hon. Bag afire around edges. Otherwise he was cooking nicely. I put him out with slight splosh of water. He look quite contented swimming around in midst of juices containing vegetables. 17 more minutes remain to cook him.

Night approach. I notice by alarm clock that time have now relapsed for Hon. Paper Bag to be completely cooked. So I take him out on platter. He look somewhat quaint. Paper bags is like spinach; they seem most beautiful when raw. It was alarmed for to see how Hon. Bag had shrunk away. He seemed insufficient for healthful family of four persons. Next time I must cook two. Howeverly, it was necessary to make most of what was, so I rolled Hon. Bag out longwise like a omelet. Then I surround him with meat and vegetables in diagram of beautiful art.

"Togo!" holla Mrs. S. W. Swingle exploding into kitchen suddenly like a gun, "Togo, what you been cooking to make my home smell like a fire-insurance?" She cough in soprano.

"I have baked you a paper bag," I report with words containing smiles. I point to plate where it was.

"Paper *what*?" she howell.

"Bag," I repartee.

She walk to platter and poke Hon. Bag irreverently with fork. She make scorn with her nose. Then she open kitchen door and urge me to it with enraged broomstick.

"I give you your choice," she say horesly. "Either you can go at once or depart immediately."

"I shall not wait that long!" I collapse with cruel expression peculiar to eagles. "If you discharge me, I shall obtain mean revenge. I shall quit."

Thusly speaking I promenade forth into unemployment. I am still there.

Hoping you are the same,
Yours truly,
Hashimura Togo.

VI
HON DISH RAG VS. THE HON. CHINA

VI HON. DISH RAG VS. THE HON. CHINA

To Editor Woman's Page who can serve Truth to homes in cups & saucers.

Hon. Dear Sir:

As nearly ago as last Wedsday I was connected to home of Mrs Jas Jones, Peru, Ind., where I am now not. My departure I shall relate.

Though refined in her appearances, this Hon. Mrs Jones is known by the dishes she keeps.

This Jones home are a continuous China closet entirely filled with it. Bloated blue bowls set in shelves amidst cups which look like History had drunk out of them. Stingy-size coffee cup to be taken after dinner are there to any extent. In presidential cabinets of mahogonish appearance she got considerable cut-up glasswear which make flashes resembling diamonds in show-case.

"Togo," she say so, "because you are intellectual Japanese, I are sure you can take care of my dishes."

"Japan are elegant chaperone for China," I absorb with chivalry.

"All my cubboards is filled with dear associates," she acknowledge. "Yonderly plates is real Japanese curios what Aunt Martha bought while travelling abroad in Chicago. Yonderly cups was handed down to me by Mr Ancestor."

"2 of them was handed down pretty hard," I say so, because handles was knock off.

"Crack and bump are considered antique," she dib, while showing me 65 soup platters containing photo of Massacheussets to show how they was once property of Henry Clay.

All them dishes look at me with prides, like I should be ashamed of my cheapness.

"Togo," deploy Hon. Mrs Jas Jones, as soonly as I was surprised as much as I could, "dishes like mine must not be washed brutally. They must be dishpanned like invalids."

"I shall be trained nurse to them so much as possible," I collapse. "Should I need toilet soap to wash such fineness?"

"Intellect are more important than soaps," she explan. "Only once did I have a servant lady with sifficient intellect to wash my dishes, but she would not remain. She are now in Colorado running for Congress."

"How shall I do it to make scientific dish-wash?" I ask to know.

She tell me this following recipe:

1st—Take one dishpan of good family, mix him with 3½ qrts. water of angry hotness until Hon. Dishpan seem quite tender.

2nd—Take one Soap of medium ripeness and mix him until he sud. Egg beater can be used if willing.

3rd—Dish-wash are now ready for it. Best Dishes to wash are them what has been smudged by foods.

4th—Drop Hon. Dish into delicious warmth of water. He will drown, but you must not pity him until he arrive entirely clean by soap.

5th—Hon. Dish will now expect warm shower bath.

6th—Wipe him until fatigued.

7th—Hon. Dish are now ready to eat another meal.

"Most delicate tool to be used in dish-wash," Mrs Jones tell with voice, "are Hon. Dishrag. He must never be neglect. He must be kep in healthful condition of athlete by continual care. He must be always clean like white gloves, so Hon. Mikerobes will not walk on him. Otherwise he will be full of feverish diseases which he will give my Dishes to pass on to us.

"To keep dishrag clean are more important duty of home life than bakery or piano lesson. You unstand this?"

"Distinctually!" I report. "But tell me this reply. What should I do if Hon. Dishrag should axidentally throw himself down on floor where dust is?"

"Oh!!" This from her. "Never—no, never at all must Dishrag be permitted to behave like that by dropping to Floor. No!! Several 1000s of person is murdered each annual year by Dishrags what has thusly flopped and caught mikerobe. O Togo, you promus me one Thing?"

"I promus."

"Promus you never permit Dishrag to flop to Floor whatever earthquake happen?"

I promus reverendly by lifting my knuckles. So she permit me to wash her dishes.

Things happens when they shouldn't. This is what make newspapers and other novels so pleasant to read. And so it was with me.

For 2 week times I work for this Mrs Jas Jones without any crisis arriving. She were so deliciously stingy of her Mrs Washington pitcher, cups & glasswear that she use 10c. store dishes of flat-iron thickness for daily use when her Husband & other folks she did not respect was home. So I needs not think of scientific dish-wash during them happy days. Yet I worry about Hon. Dishrag continuously, because I was afraid he might strike some germs. How could I keep him clean while washing plates with him?

So I wash plates with my rude hands and hung Hon. Dishrag to clean peg where he would not get soil. Hon. Mrs seem entirely pleasant when she see the trained-nurse appearance of that Hon. Rag. I feel sure I should last there until old age.

But one afternoon was different, Mr Editor, because Mr & Mrs Budhammer, grandfather, dog, 2 Aunts and assorted children arrive up for lunching. Add to this Mr & Mrs Jas Jones and you have considerable dish-wash for poor Togo. And what did Hon. Mrs Jones do? She arrange on table all her important dishwear for fashionable appearance. Andrew Jackson butter-platter was there; Wm Shakespeare pattern plates with golden dots; Mr Ancestor's glasswear in cut-up shapes of aggrevated beauty—every scarce China you could imagine was set there for folks to eat so I could wash it.

Them guests was very hospitable to Mr & Mrs Jas Jones. They say them plates was so beautiful they make the food taste better than it was. They make happy conversations while Aunt Elizabeth tell about her husband who died from Rheumatism on the brains. Everybody speak of subject he like most. Hon. Mrs Jones tell mean things she could say to neighbours and Mr Budhammer describe how happy he was before marriage. Thus do social interchange make joyful friendship!

After slight coffee was drunk all rose up and eloped forthly to verandah where all could smoke amidst fancy work and tell gossip anecdotes.

But I was not invited to this. It was now my important time for dish-wash when I should show all the science of my soul with that valuable China & other cups.

I take all fashionable Ancestor dishes from table and pile to kitchen. I was deliciously skilful like a bricklayer as I stacked cup on plate etc., until I got one nice crockery mountain 6¼ feet high with Mrs Martha Washington pitcher standing top-tip of 16 glasses looking beautiful like History monument. It are remarkable how many dishes can pile on each other without falling off.

I cooked some hot water by boiling it. Then I obtain Hon. Dishpan & satisfy him full of hot water, adding soap until it seem comfortable. Nextly I remove Hon. Dishrag from window where he enjoy sunshine by looking into garden. With reverent fingers, so I should not mix mikerobes with him, I flop him to Dishpan. Then I splunge my hands into that sud and stir continuously.

Mr Editor, did you ever stand with your fingers in warm dishwater thinking Thoughts. Such kind hotness surrounds your wrists that you feel poetical and disengaged. I am not suprised that so many servant ladies is such sweet singers while dish-washing. Their souls cannot remain hardened while their fingers is soaking in such pleasant soap sud.

Suddenly, while thusly I stood, great confusion came to my brain. I remember what Hon. Mrs told me about keeping Hon. Dishrag away from dirt. Then I look to that pile of Dishes. Some of them, though rare & expensive, was all disarranged by colours of food and blackberry pie. No! I could not enrage my sweet Boss Lady by touching sacred rag to that!

So I lift Hon. Dishrag from soap-water, ring him out with loving care and begin shake him so no rude germs would remain from contact with sud. I make 2 complete shakes and was starting Shake No 3—when O! Hon. Dishrag escape from my finger and start flopping to floor! Terrors! This must not happen!! How raged Hon. Mrs would be if this respected rag should catch some dust against her stric orders!

With immediate quickness I make extreme grab sidewards, snatching rapidly like cats catching grasshopper. I got him—between thumbs and elbows I caught that escaping Rag, but in thusly behaving—whop! My physique collapsed against entire dish-pile and following climax happened:

SMASHES!!!!

With noise peculiar to a crockery store falling off an Alp all that expensive China & glasswear elapse to floor and mix itself into broken hash like a battlefields after cannon shoots it. You could not tell cups from plates in that crackery of crockery.

"O murder from ignorant Japanese!" holla Hon. Mrs Jas Jones & Company making inrush to kitchen. "Alive sakes, you have dropped my entire home!"

And yet I smiled.

"Why you laugh like hickory Indian when all I have is broke?" she otter.

"Mrs Madam," I corrode brave like frozen Napoleon, "I acknowledge the brokerage which I made amidst Hon. Dishes. Yet you needs not worry. I have saved your Dishrag."

Human nature are very doggish, Mr. Editor. Though I prove to that Lady how heroic I was she kill all my answers with her replies while Hon. Mr Jones toss me forth from that jobs. With rabid hat I bid farewell without saying so. I are just another hero walking in homeless direction because of shipwreck.

Hoping you are the same
Yours truly
HASHIMURA TOGO.

VII
A DAY AT HOME

VII A DAY AT HOME

To Editor Woman's Page who is honest man, therefore at home when he is.

Dearest Sir:

My next escape was from employment of Mrs. Clarence Calicutt, Siberia, N. Y. This lady was very highly esteamed. She practise theosophy on her mind and make society acquaintance with frequent ladies. She had the most deceptive behaviour of any personality I ever employed to boss me. Her voice was half in half. One end of it was sweet, but the other end contained considerable quinine. The bitterish end was all I ever saw. For instancely, in curl-paper hour of early morning she would arise upward from breakfast and say, "Togo, why you so dub this day? Are you foolish or merely brainless?" Hashly she spoke it.

Jing-jing from telephone.

"Hello—are that you, Clara? How charmed you are! Yes, honey, I should seem very much obliged!" Sweetly she used her voice.

"Why you speak lemons to me and honey to telephone?" I asked to know.

"Because," she report, "there are two ways of talking—one way for servants, other way for telephone."

"Sometimes I wish you would talk to me like a telephone," I require, saddishly.

One raindrop morning this Mrs. Calicutt approach to me and report. "Togo, I am at home to-morrow afternoon."

"Will you be more at home then than you are now?" I ask it.

"I are not at home now," she dib, snubbly.

"How confused!" I magnify. "You mean tell me you are not at home when I see you there standing?"

"Truthfully I speak it." This from her.

"Then maybe you could be elsewhere when you are at home?" I collapse.

"Quite conveniently," she otter. "I know some several ladies who frequently go ottomobile riding on days when they are at home."

"America are full of customs," I report, enjoying headache in my understanding.

"I am at home on second and fifth Wednesdays of September, June, and January," she speak onwards. "I choose them difficult dates so folks can amuse themselves calculating when they will see me next. It are not fashionable for a lady to be seen too frequently at her residence."

"It would require train despatchers and astronomers to calculate when to call with cards," I report. She make no visible reply to that.

"To-morrow is my Wednesday," she describe, pridefully.

"Will you keep this date all to yourself?" I ask to know.

"Not by no means I won't!" she snudge. "I have invite considerable guests for slight tea-drunk. I asked them for 4. P. M. So I shall expect them about 6:30."

"How much people you expect, if any?" I require.

"Folks who comes to afternoon tea-drunk are like mice what comes to traps. You never can tell how many you will catch. Sometimes refreshment-bait are entirely wasted without a nibble. Sometime they come in such quantities they carries off the trap. Sometime, when you ask folks to tea, they behave shyly like rabbits. Sometimes they make forward stampede like mules, all attempting to rush at once."

"Then you cannot give me any statistic to estimate how many persons will arrive up to your Wednesday to-morrow?"

"I asked 80 persons. Perhapsly 8 or 200 will arrive. Who knows what?"

"Do all them persons expect to eat from your food?" I asked, for cold eyebrows.

"Folks does not come to teas to eat entirely, but to eat somewhat," she reproof. "Mutton chops, oyster, and soup would seem too heavyweight for such festival. Yet they would act disappointed and peevly if they could not have some lightweight refreshment."

"Ham plus eggs would do for them, perhapsly?" I snuggest.

"Nothing would seem more toothless for such occasion," she growell. "Slight nibble of cakes, slight squench of chocolate will be too sufficient with conversation. Therefore, I ask you to attend to refreshments for to-morrow. Please prepare following lightweight foods for them:

5 doz. devilish ham samditches.

5 doz. nutty samditches confused with cheeze.

5 doz. letus samditches containing salad.

12 qts. chocolate drunk.

A large chorus of cakes, McAroons, candies & other meatsweets in confusion."

I done what she said, Mr. Editor. You cannot imagine with all your printer's ink how I enslaved myself preparing them samditches for her festival. All morning of Wednesday I stood gashing bread with knives till I manufactured so much of that lay-between food that it stood in bulk. Piles of devilish ham samditches stood around near heaps of nutty cheeze samditches, resembling sky scrapers looking at Washington Monuments with jealous expression.

All that A. M. Hon. Mrs. Calicutt rosh everywhere doing something to furniture & draping smilax buds from pictures to resemble greenery. At lunching hour she appear very disjointed and say, "Aunts of Columbus Society holds annual social this P. M. at Methodist Church. Maybe I shall not be able to catch many folks from this." Sadness stood in her voice.

Hon. Clarence Calicutt, husband to her, retire homeward by 3:11 train and report, "What could be more nuisansical for business man than pink tea?"

At 4:10 P. M. all was prepare. Cousin Florence arrive for pore tea. Mrs. Clarence Calicutt set in central middle of room making her clothes look very social. Hon. Clarence Calicutt wear frockaway coat and require, "Can I smoke?" whenever spoken to. Cousin Florence crouch behind tea-earn with expectful expression peculiar to sailors before battle. But nothing arrived yet.

At 4:59 come jing-jing to door bell. Mrs. Calicutt arrange her smile, Cousin Florence set upright, & Hon. Clarence go to window where he attempt to look neglectful.

I elope to door with desirable expression peculiar to butlers. With noble position of heels and elbows I ope door. What see? There stood one (1) Armenian peddle-man offering $2 tablecloths for $3.57. I enclose Hon. Door befront of his face.

"This are most excited afternoon of my career," depress Hon. Calicutt, smoking cigars out of window so as not to fumigate curtains.

Mrs. Calicutt make several petrified replies.

At hour of 5:68 P. M. Rev. Mr. Horse W. Dill come in. He never could afford to miss repasts anywheres because of his shrinking salary.

"All world seem to be at Aunts of Columbus reception this afternoon," he say for diplomacy.

"I notice it," dib Hon. Mrs. "I just remain home merely by accident to-day & so glad you come."

I offer him 86 samditches. He ate 13 and 1 qrt. chocolate. He depart at 7:46 filled with delicious refreshment. After that Hon. Clarence, Mrs. Clarence, and Cousin Florence draw near together & gaze morbidly at them samditches piled in towers.

For week latter, evening dinner at home of Calicutt contained following programme:

SOUP

Didn't have none.

ENTREE

Chocolate. Samditches containing cheeze.

ROAST

Devilish ham samditches. Nutty samditches.

SALAD

Letus samditches.

DESERT

McAroons, cakes, more chocolate, & whatever else.

Hon. Mrs. Calicutt and Cousin Florence ate this table of contents without complaining voice. Ladies is often thusly—they do not desire real food when they can be economical. But me & Mr. Calicutt begin to feel very illegal when we look at them samditches which must be ate. Frequently Mr. Calicutt telephone home that his board of directors had appendicitis, therefore he must stay in town for dine. I forgive him this deception.

Three weeks pass off. Then come fifth Wednesday when Mrs. Calicutt must again be at home for friends.

"Togo," she pronounce that morning, "I have invite 120 complete persons and expect to enjoy quite a stampede this P. M. Please multiply your former programme of samditches by twice."

"I shall do so," I deploy.

Yet my soul determined to do elsewise. Why must I again clutter that household with sky-scraping piles of samditches which nobody came to eat except Rev. Mr. Dill who had merely appetite for 13? No! If Hon. Mrs. Calicutt was too foolish in her brain to keep from that extravagance, then I should save her from it. I should merely make 13 samditches and 1 qrt. chocolate, sifficient for Hon. Dill. Yet I should make my Boss Lady think I was preparing great quantities. This deceptiveness require great heroism.

"Togo," say her, coming to kitchen in early P. M., "Are bread & devilish ham and letus and marionaise dressing and chocolate all ready to be executed in vast quantities?"

"They are faithfully prepared," I pronounce with talented dishonesty.

"120 guests often feel very edible, so do it plenty," she acknowledge, eloping away.

At 3 o'clock I manufacture 13 samditches and 1 qrt. chocolate. That was all we could afford to give Mr. Dill.

"Where are refreshments, please?" requesh Mrs. Calicutt when 4 P. M. was there.

"I keep them cooly concealed in dark place where staleness will not arrive to them," I report, looking sly like roosters. She too busy preparing smilax buds to know how much money I saved her by not manufacturing food for guests who wouldn't come.

At 4:63 P. M. I notice something which make my eyes alarmed. With tense puffing honk-music and wheel-rumble, 47 ottomobiles, buggies, motorcycles, & go-carts arrive up to house all together like sheep. They hitch up by front gate. Why was they came? O look see!! 118 complete persons of every imaginable age & sect got out and make jing-jing to door bell.

One horble thought roshed to my ears. All them folks was coming expecting to eat Rev. Dills' 13 samditches and 1 qrt. chocolate! I was blame for my economy. What must I do? My heart turned pale while hysteria filled my elbows. Already I could hear glad-you-came sound by Mrs. Calicutt while that hungry mobb make rosh through parlour room amidst disagreeable laughter.

Swish-swish! It was Mrs. Calicutt's silk footsteps coming.

"Togo," she whisper with stage-voice, introducing her head at kitchen, "where is immediate food for 120 persons?"

"Here, please," I report with quaker knees, poking forth them 13 samditches on plate.

Shrieks by her. Deep breathing and 4 sobs. I withdraw myself away from there before she should make a scenery. I slid myself from back door softly like cats walking over ice-cycles.

I felt very sorry for Mrs. Calicutt losing me like that, but when I reached trolley-road where I got on, I felt less pity. After all, there was ½ fraction of corned beef and 1 qrt. milk in ice-box, so them 120 At Homers needs not go entirely destitute from food. Maybe they would enjoy that, if conversation was sifficiently fascinating. For what-say famus Japanese philosopher, Oysta-san? He say, "In good company crusts tastes rich, but in bore company ice-cream seems awful poor."

Hoping you are the same,
Yours truly,
HASHIMURA TOGO.

VIII
PETS

VIII PETS

To Editor Woman's Page who do so much to make home-life less homely.

Hon. Dear Sir:

Mrs. Benjoman Barnum of Pyramid Park, Penn, is the latest lady to turn me loose. Whether she are a relationship to Hon. P. T. Barnum (deceased) I am not aware enough to say, but she have got a very menagerie mind. Her home is a tame zoo full of animals. I am sure, if she had a bigger parlour, she would keep a elephant.

"Togo," she report to me when she hired me off the Fineheimer Employment Bureau, "nothing make home so lively as several Pets."

"I notice this," is bright reply for me. "You are the most pettish lady I ever worked for."

She did not seem to assimilate them words I said, yet they was truthful. Her home resembled Mr. Noah's Houseboat in variety of 4-foot, 2-foot & 1-foot beasts it contained. By actual stastistics Mrs. Barnum possessed the following list of live Pets, which she support from sweethearted reasons of kindness:

1 Dog of waggish ways & barking vocabulary. His name was Julius Siezer, but Neighbours call him "Git Out!" because he dug mines in their flower beds. I forgot his nationality, but his complexion was Irish; 1 Cat entitled Florence who earned her food by purring for it. Her feet was deliciously full of thorns; 1 Parrot called Robt. Burns because his soul was in his talk; 1 cannary-bird name Dick. He didn't seem to have no resemblance to his name; 2 Goldfish Twins, Harry & Carry who spent their days idly swimming in glass & saying nothing.

Mrs. Barnum formerly had one husband who went dead. I congratulate him.

When all those Pets is going at once, dog-bark, cat-mew, parrot-shriek and cannary-bird warbul, it sound like a brass band composed of dish-pans & steam whistles.

"I love my dum friends," explan Mrs. Barnum to me with kind-eye expression.

"I love them most when they are most dum," I repartee, suppressing my ears from those scrambled sounds. "If you could teach those goldy-fishes to sing, the harmonium would be complete."

While I said thus that dog Siezer approach up and bit me on leg.

"He do this in fun," say Mrs. Barnum.

"So glad to hear!" I negotiate. "Dogs never hurts so much when they bite humorously."

"If you wish for to be employed in this home you must be keeper as well as housekeeper," she tell off. "Promptly at noon o'clock each day the annimals must be fed. Each have his peculiaristic diet, which he crave for health. Siezer must have bone, Florence require cream, Robt. Burns expect apple, Dick ask for seed, while Harry & Carry demand fishfood. I should rather see anything than that my Pets go hungry."

I assimilate her words and do what best I can. It require tack and courage to chaperone those Pets. They are all cannibles by appetite and would love to eat each other for their food qualities. When Hon. Seizer, the dog, are unloosed from his mesh he start forthly with waggish expression of tail and attemp to gobble Hon. Florence, the cat. This delusive mammal are too speedful for that dog, so she elope with hissy noise to mantel-piece where she set growelling with enlarged fur. When Hon. Siezer are absent attending other duties, Hon. Florence set hour by hour gazing upward at Hon. Dick, the cannary-bird, and wishing she had a baloon to obtain him with. When I approach this talented cat she make purr-song and slide around my ankles, requesting that I should give her Dick for lunch. I must refuse, out of politeness for Dick. Sometime Hon. Florence prefer fish. Then she walk up wallpaper like a fly and thusly arrive to shelf where Harry & Carry are swimming selfishly around in their toy ocean.

Hon. Robt. Burns, the parrot, are less particular. He like any sort of food, as long as it are alive. One day he observe me and say with tender squawk, "O darling, come, come to your own sailor boy!" I come. When I approach sifficiently close, Oh, nipp! Hon. Parrot remove off ¼ from my ear and set there looking satisfied. I sorrow to think he could talk so tender, yet act so tough!

Last Thursday A. M. Mrs. Barnum approach to me. She did not know it was my last day with her. Neither did I. Life is so surprised!

"Togo," she instruct, "I am going over to Aunt Jane's to set by a sick bedside."

"Are Aunt Jane diseased?" I require.

"No. It are her cat what has influenza of the diagram," she tell. "I shall be gone 1 hour time. Remember, while I are away my pets must be fed. Do not neglect this. I would rather anything than that they should go hungry."

I give her my promissory word.

As soonly as she had went I begin task of furnishing bill-of-fare for her zoo. To Siezer I give bone, to Florence cream. They accept this without thanks. Then I donate one apple to Hon. Robt. Burns who sung, "Every morn I bring thee violets" and attemp to chew off thumb from me. Everything was affectionate as usual.

Nextly I go to shelf where Harry & Carry are bathing in glass. I took them to table where I irrigated them with fresh water. I was just feeding them slight lunch of delicious bait when———SCRASH!!!

From next room I heard Hon. Robt. Burns say distinctly, "If you love me, darling, tell me with your eyes!" So I knew he was doing some sort of murder.

I rosh in. Oh!! what sight I seen. That parrot-fowell had escaped away from his roost and lept upward to goldy cage where Hon. Dick was making opera with voice. With talented grabb that conversational chicken had shipwrecked Hon. Cage and deposited Hon. Dick-bird to floor. When I met Hon. Parrot he was hen-picking that talented songster. I attemp to arrest him for his brutality, but he attach my finger with his eagle mouth. I was removing him from this when, SCRUNSH!!!

Loud crashy of glass from next room. I rosh forwards. I was just in time to be too late. Hon. Florence had pushed glassy residence of Hon. Goldfishes to floor and was dieting on those gilt swimmers. She look thankful while she make gollup of Harry. She also ate Carry ½, but when I remove remainder from her she make reproachful growell and snagg me with thorny foot. I attempt to restore Hon. Carry who was fainted away, when—BOW WOWS!!!

Hon. Siezer approach to scene determined to obtain food supply from that cat. Hon. Florence rosh up curtains with angry sizz peculiar to sky-rockets when she seen that dogged approach. Hon. Dog smile up at Hon. Cat and Hon. Cat smile down at Hon. Dog.

While thusly they stood Hon. Dick awoke up from where he lay and limped forth on shabby wings. He give 3 and ½ sorry peeps and flitter to fireplace where he flew up flue.

Just at that instantaneous moment Hon. Robt. Burns arrive in with rawcuss yellup, and hooked his feet to chandelier where he hung suspended downside-up like a umberella. Dog & Cat continue to gaz up & down at each other like Romeo & Juliet.

"Should old acquaintance be forgot?" require Hon. Parrot, twirling his head 3 times in circular manner.

I had no time to reply to this inquisitiveness. It were nearly time for Mrs. Barnum to return homeward and I was full of timid fright for fear she might notice how badly her Pets was mixed among themselves. I did not feel sifficient to meet her angry rage.

So I handed my resignation to myself.

On hasty piece of paper I wrote:

> Esteamed Mrs. Madam:—when nextly you see Togo he will be gone. So will your golden-fish & cannary-bird. But I will not be gone where they are, because your Pets do not crave me for food. I are not sensitive about this neglect. When you left me this morning you say so that you thought their appetites was failing. I could not dishcover that dangerous symptom. All they need was change of food. If ever you find them refusing eat in the future, do what I done—turn them loose on each other. If you wish to find Harry & Carry, search Miss Florence. If you can not dishcover Miss Florence when you get back, search Mr. Siezer. I am sorry to go, but glad I went.

I attach this information secretively to door-handle. From inside of house I could hear Hon. Siezer making coon-tree noises responded to by war-cry voice of Miss Florence. From top-tip of chandelier Hon. Robt. Burns was reporting peevly, "Fare-bye, for I must leave thee! One parting kiss—ar, ar, ar!!"

I sneek silently away on velvet feetsteps, feeling like one Spartan boy who done his duty by escaping from it.

Hoping you are the same,
Yours truly,
Hashimura Togo.

IX
WASHING WINDOWS

IX WASHING WINDOWS

To Editor Woman's Page whose mind is glass which shoots daylight into Subjects.

Dear Sir:—

Until quite recently of yore I remained in the suburbs of Pennsylvania at home of Mrs Nero Fits Gibb, where I stayed as long as I did.

It was because of windows that I was exploded off from that lovely situation of employment. Next job of work I shall hitch myself to some house which do not contain any of those glass encumbents.

I tell you this narrative.

That Hon. Mrs Fits Gibb reside in one large mahogany house containing sifficient windows to see everything through. Bay windows occur at moments when least expected; skylights peep from roof with expression peculiar to pair of spectacles. That house has got windows all over its face from its chin to its forehead, and every door are confused by glass stained brightly to resemble colours.

"Togo," explan Hon. Mrs to me, "I are very fond of fresh daylight."

"You have caged nearly all there is," I corrode for politeness while gazing at 13 doz. windows surrounding.

"When doing nothing," she explan, "it shall be your duty to wash them windows with careful soap. This will make them more light."

"I am hired for light work," I suggest. "What are most scientific way to bathe these glass eyes of your home?"

"Most artistic window-wash can be obtained with a ladder and a bucket," she deploy. "Also rags must be used including soap and gymnastics. Take these materials to window requiring cleanliness and rub until exhausted. Continue this massage on next window and therefore on. Industry must be had. Do not abandon a pain of glass until he shine with brilliancy resembling genius."

So I go do what she say. I got ladder, I obcured rags, I obtained sudds bucket according to orders Hon. Mrs Fits Gibb gave me. So farly so goodly.

Grasping ladder on my shoulder with military expression I walk around Hon. House to pick out one window what appear good natured & easy. More I looked less I could decide. That Hon. House continue to gaze at me sternly like one octopus with 1000 glass eyes. At lastly I find one pompus bay window what set over front door presenting swelled appearance peculiar to Presidents.

I look thoughtfully upwards and make philosophy by myself.

"Window-wash are like Success," I commute. "It are most pleasant to begin at the top and work downward. Therefore I shall begin by soaping this important outlook."

So I amount up ladder with Hon. Bucket inclosed in my knuckles and numberous rags embraced by my suspenders. Uply and more uply I march until I was there looking Hon. Window in the face. So I begin to wash him.

Mr Editor, the simplest things in life seems the most simplest when they are not. Do it not seem easy to your educational brain for a Japanese Schoolboy to carry sudds up ladder and apply him to window pain by rubs of rag? And yet such work are full of complex.

No sooner I begin attacking this job than I dishcover how Hon. Window Wash must be like a juggle in a circus. To obtain myself on that ladder I must clasp my toes with carefulness resembling stork, at same time I must balance Hon. Bucket by elbow, hold Hon. Rags in teeth and splatter Hon. Window with what fingers I had left. In the meanwhile, what was Hon. Soap doing? When he got wet his nature changed and he imagined he was a snake. He would not stay where he was, but amuse himself by slipping off from everywheres I put him. Every time he fall, I must dutifully ascend down that ladder, pick him from grass, carefully descend upwards again and attempt to hang him somewheres where he would not make an eel of himself. I never seen soap so full of slyness.

And yet I work onwards in spite of him. With delicious accuracy I threw sudds on Hon. Window till he seem to weep tears. Then I wipe him elaborously with rag. Yet more I wipe, less beautiful he appear. Greyness cover him with streaks. More rubbs. Stripes of smudge confuse that glass. More lather I put on. Yet Hon. Window continue to look dull & bilious. I massage him up and down with greased elbow until it was nearly sunset of p. m. O discouraged! If diamonds is so hard to polish, I are not surprised that nobody but policemen can afford such jewelery.

Pretty soonly I could hear voice of Hon. Mrs saluting me crossly from below down.

"Togo," she report, "you have been 2 hours in labour of work. How many windows have you bathed completely?"

"Nearly one," I corrode boastfully.

"If it take you 2 hours to wash nearly one window, how long would it take you to cleansify 211 glass pains in this house?" This arithmatic from her.

"422 hours," I reject brightly. "If you will loaned me paper & pencill, I shall be happy to estimate how many weeks that makes."

"Xmas will arrive before then," she agnosticate with bang of door.

I could not understood her repartee. Maybe she intend to give me Xmas present.

When fatigue was too plenty for more exercise I stand on climax of that ladder holding sudds bucket in thoughtful position. Great thoughts can be obtained in such high altitudes, thusly perched with excelsior feeling of brain. Leaning against glass forehead of that bay window I could observe Nature acting as usual amidst houses where residences was. Walking amongst those houses I could observe bill collectors, insurance agents and neighbours—which show that Trouble come wherever folks resides. "Life are similar to such scenery," I say for smart quotation.

While thusly I argued, some ottomobile wheels could be heard walking below in front of house. I look downly and observe very fashionable appearance of society—one bloated gas-machinery stopping up near feet of ladder while one complete lady enwrapped in Arctic mouse-skins fur sat there talking Waldorf language to a chauffer of military pattern. I could tell she was 400 by actual count.

"Hennery," she say to Hon. Chauffer, "ring door and pronounce that Mrs. Diggle Clodd have arrived for slight calling visit on Mrs. Fits Gibb."

"I do so!" This from Hon. Hennery.

While Hon. Hennery was making rings by door, I lean from ladder and observe the elegance of that financial lady as she flopped amidst coloured padding and showed the splendid millinary of her hat.

Great excitement by me. She were not beautiful as ladies go—and some ladies goes considerable. Her hair was red like a blushing brick and her face seem too wealthy to agree with anybody. Yet I was enraptured to be standing above so much money.

I perch on ladder to imitate birds. Pretty soonly Hon. Hennery, containing expensive boots, report back.

"Hon. Mrs. Gibbs are here where she is," he acknowledge while opening ottomobile door so Hon. Lady could alight down richly. Queens act thusly when getting out of ships. I could observe the fluttering ostriches on top of her millinary head. How expensive to estimate!

When she was snuggling forth in direction of front door, I must lean very crooked backwards for see what was. I could not tell how it happen, but when leastly expected—O knock! Hon. Soap slyly slip forth from window-sill where he was setting and flop to hat of Mrs. Diggle Clodd!!! Great mixture of plumage ensued while feathers drop with confusion resembling 2 roosters fighting in a cyclone.

"Oh Hennery! Look upwards and see what!" she shreech.

Hennery do so, and while thusly he gazed my elbow disjoint himself and O swash!!! That suds bucket flop forwards & spill 2 complete gals soap-water on top of his elegance.

He show bitter expression peculiar to persons standing under Niagara.

"Who do it?" holla Hon. Hennery & Hon. Mrs.

"I no do it!" were lawyer reply for me. "Hon. Bucket must be guilty."

"Are you not manager for that bucket?" require Hon. Hennery.

"How could I tell when he is going to shoot?" I narrate.

"Hennery!!" she gubble, "elope up ladder and pluck that impertinence down!"

Mr. Editor, I are a tame Japanese, yet when I observe gentleman in uniform descending up ladder with warfare expression, all the Port Arthur of my nationality come out.

"Hara kiri!" I acknowledge to Hon. Chauffer while shooting remnants of sudds-water straight at his profile. He look very bathhouse—yet he still continue to approach.

"When I obtain you—" he pronounce, making a grab to heel.

"When you get me I shall be elsewhere," I defy. Thusly speaking I leap into the face of that bay window and arrive inside of bedroom with loudy crashes. Somebody below-stairs yell, "Burglar!"—but I knew I could not be a burglar and be so noisy. Hon. Hennery continue to approach up ladder. In anxious escape I jump over 11 chairs, 2½ beds with numerous etcetera.

In a soon moment I could observe wet headware of Hon. Hennery encroaching through window where he enter with rebound. I make talented dodge to hallway where I bang door & lock him, thus encircling Hon. Chauffer with his wrath.

Below downstairs I could hear Hon. Mrs Clodd talking mustard to Hon. Mrs Gibb. I could hear angry voices walking upstairs.

If I lost any time I must do so quickly. I trot backwards down hall. From window in rearward bedroom I seen one porch-escape from which I flew like aeroplanes. I make down shoot to ground while Hon. Mrs. holla from window.

"Togo," she yall, "you are requested never to look into my house again!"

"Those residing in a houseful of windows should look out for themselves," I nudge back walking away in sections.

Hoping you are the same, yours truly,
Hashimura Togo.

X
PAPER-HANGING

X PAPER-HANGING

To Editor Home & Ladies Page who realise how wallpaper are like friendship: sometime he stick right, and sometime he don't.

Dear Mr:

Mrs Bertha Mac Frenzie, a very medium lady residing in Boston, Conn., disemployed me recently from happy home. I was very satisfactory help to her until following anecdote happen to me.

Mrs Mac Frenzie's only extravagance are her stingyness. Careful in most everything, she become extra reckless when attempting to save 9c. Her thoughts are filled with skimmed milk & slaughterhouse steak. I am suprised Hon. U. S. Government do not hire her to saw off High Cost of Living before he start to grow any taller. I know because I seen it.

"Togo," she require of me, "too much wealth is lavished in that soup you make. He is too thick."

"If he become thinner he will faint away," I warn out.

"Soup will stand considerable starvation and yet seem hearty," she deploy. So I do so.

Last Wedsday she approach up to me with arms full of roll-up material.

"I have dishcovered now so I can save 9$!" she deploy with glee-club voice.

"Such saving may involve great expense," I corrode brightly.

She neglect my chivalry.

"I am determined to paper bedroom of upstairs," she rake off. "This shall be done by home-made labour. These wallpapers what I got only cost 10c. per roll, thusly saving 1$. Experienced paper hangmen require 4$ per day. It take 2 such to paste a room properly. I shall employ you for nothing to do this valuable task, thusly saving 8$. Therefore, I save 1$ + 8$ = 9$."

"What clever stingyness you think up!" I oblate. No response from her.

She led me upwards to bedroom where that job must be.

"Have you any knowledge of paper-hanging?" she ask it.

"I never before attended such a lynching," was answer I make.

"I show you how is," she reciprocate. So she lay down following tools on floor where I could see:

> 12 bundles wallpaper of blue complexions tattooed with beauty resembling cauliflowers flirting with grapes.
>
> 1 complete bucket filled with undigested dough to make it stick by.
>
> Confused rags to pat with.
>
> 1 ironing board to stick paper on top of.
>
> 1 ladder to lift paper on when hanging him.
>
> 1 shears for cut up paper by.

"Firstly," correspond Hon. Mrs with shears, "you must take Hon. Paper thusly and manicure edges."

She make cut-up with shears for show how.

"Nextly you must measure wall with very careful tailorship, so Hon. Paper will fit neatly like a coat."

I observe her did it.

"Nextly make chop off to Hon. Paper at place where he fits. Then lay him on ironing-board and lather his back completely with dough from Hon. Bucket."

By brush she do so.

"Next Hon. Paper are ready to be lynched. Raise him tenderly by both ears while climbing ladder and spread him on wall with smoothness resembling butter. If he refuse to lay still, pat him lovingly with rags."

She teach me that science while I stand gast to observe her skilful thumbs.

"Can you do this jobs?" she require to know.

"Elaborately," I confiscate.

And yet I were not aware that paperhanging are like poetry, marriage, and other games—deliciously easy to look at, but less easy to do.

So Hon. Mrs Mac Frenzie depart away for make society elsewheres and I was left alonesome with that paper. Firstly I look at him long time admiring the extreme art of his complexion. I could not realise how so many grapes and cauliflowers could get together without being confused. Admiration by me!

Then I start some industry. Firstly I cut sifficient chunk of this flowery decoration so he will fit wall. This were aggrevated task to do, because when I unroll him to make measure, he roll back with rat-trap expression and burst my thumbs. I can only make him behave by putting my feet on him while holding him down to ironing board. Pretty soonly, by extreme skill of swashing, I manage to plaster his back with dough like Mrs Mac Frenzie told me.

Mr Editor, to lubricate wallpaper with paste are difficult art like greasing snakes with cold cream. There are so much longness to him that he can do one thing with front end, while accomplishing otherwise with tail. So it was. Onwards & onwards I continue to paste Hon. Wall Paper while he uncoil to any extent. Pretty soonly front end of him were drooping to carpet, and yet I continue to brush his back.

At lastly he were entirely moist and ready to be lynched. With delicious politeness I pick him up by corners and start to descend up ladder with brave expression of fireman saving actresses. But when I was nearly upward I discover one sad event. Lower end of Hon. Paper refuse to be elevated. For what reason? For reason because he had pasted himself to carpet and clung there with stupidity resembling cats.

"I must domineer this wallpaper with my personality," I say to self. So I lift both elbows strongly in attempting to jerk him from carpet. With expression of helpless peev peculiar to angle-worms he tore in two. ½ of his flowery egotism drop stickfully to carpet. Other ½ remain affectionately clinging to my lower legs where he remain, however much I beg him to desist off.

Wallpaper, Mr Editor, resemble some female Ladies, beautiful in their complexions, but very sidewise when least expected.

So on that ladder stood me & Hon. Wall Paper clinging together like Romeo & Juliet, but not mentioning love poems. The more I loosened, the more he tightened. By time I was able to disjoint him from my legs, he had fell affectionately on my chest where he make behaviour peculiar to postage stamps. Yet I did not enrage. Diplomacy frequently succeeds where boxing gloves are footless. So I decide to conquer Hon. Wall Paper by kindness. Gently, almost shyly I ripped him from my chest at same moment so arranging my wrists that I could detach him away from my legs. Oh joyful! Soonly he were divorced from me and swinging entirely free where I hold him aloftward by his ears. This were fine moment to paste him suddenly before he understood what I was doing.

So I make quick jump at wall with determined elbows. But Hon. Paper were more sudden than me. Before I could think he looped himself sidewise and became stuck on himself.

This make curious perdiclement. Try as I should to pry him apart, he become more and more absorbed in his personality. By this time his blue complexion were so confused by finger-prints that he look entirely Bertillon. It would require mathematics to tell which was right side of him and which wrong.

Then I decide to kill him at once and try another. So I clump him up in wad resembling laundry and cast him outward by window.

This were cruel thing to do, but there are some things which look best when you can't see them.

Next piece paper I try were less backward. He stand very tame & quiet while I measure him. He sat still and wagg his tail while I paste him by brush. I love very much to think how polite he act. Pretty soonly he were ready to be hung, so I elope up ladder filled with happy thoughts to think how happy Mrs Mac Frenzie would get when she seen her wall so broke out with buds. With art expression peculiar to Michael Angelo I upraise Hon. Wall Paper aboveward. He lay still and quiet like eggs. Adjusting my thumbs I was entirely ready to paste him when—O pounce!

Oozing damp glue from his annointed back he suddenly fall on my head and surround me where I stood on that ladder.

It were like riding an airship while being buried in a tent full of mucilage. It were like sleeping between sheets of fly-paper.

I were in a very perdiculous position. Must I leap from ladder, thusly bursting neck so far from Japan? Or must I stood there and be gradually smothered up in mural decorations?

I could feel sticky substance drooping from my hair & eyebrows. I stood on my perch like a blind bird.

"What this?" I could see a voice beside me saying so. It were Mrs Mac Frenzie, I could told by the claws in her speech.

"Gug!" I response with all the language I could. I knew she was observing my wallpaper face.

"Come down at oncely!" she holla. I obey by tittering backwards from my perch and walking on air which had a hole in it thus permitting me to fall 12 feet to central room where most of the furniture was, including Hon. Paste Bucket which got confused in everything else including me.

When I pick myself uply from that rumpus, my head was intruding from wallpaper hood like a fanciful millinary.

Hon. Floor were covered by paste, paper, and relics of where I fell.

"You done nice job!" snarred Hon. Mrs who stood in midst.

"I shall do better next place," I recover.

"You have papered everything in the room except the wall," she dib sarcastly.

"I are going to paper that next," are answer for me.

"There shall never not be no Next!" she squabble, while poking me forthly into frostbite of street.

There I stood in coldness without any other overcoat except wall paper I wore.

So I slushed saddishly to trolley remembering words of Hon. Mild Standish. "If you want a thing done wrong, do it yourself!"

Hoping you do so, Yours truly,
Hashimura Togo.

XI HON.
GLADYS OBTAIN MATRIMONY

XI HON. GLADYS OBTAIN MATRIMONY

To Editor Woman's Page, who do so much to make family life less lonesome.

Dear Mr Sir:—

Home of Hon. Samule Scott, East Orange, N. J., is one of the nicest homes from which I ever was discharged from. When I first went there to work that family contained following list of persons:

> Mrs Scott
> Mr ”
> Miss ” (retired).

This Miss Scott were young lady of 20 years complete beauty. O such smiling hair & blond eyes! How well her complexion matched her costume! Before her marriage her name was Gladys, but I are not sure what she is called now, as each American girl must change her name when she get married. This is very confusing custom to Japanese boy. I was working for that Scott family when that Hon. Gladys obtained matrimony. I never seen an American wedding before. Now I realise why so many people in these U. S. object to being married more than once.

Hon. Scott, who has been a father to Gladys all her life, arrived up to me last Tuesday P. M. and say fidgetfully,

"Togo," he say, "there will be a wedding in this house next Satday & I wish you would be as stylish as possible in passing food. You must appear fashionable in every way, because it are customary on such occasions to look more wealthy than you are."

"Are you going to be married again, Hon. Sir?" I ask with chivalry.

"Not if I could avoid it!" he say peevly. "It is my daughter Gladys who I shall give away."

"To who will you donate this charming lady?" I ask out.

"Hon. Charlie Sweetberry will be the blushing bridebroom," he pronounce. "You remember Charlie who arrive here more & more frequently bearing flowers?"

"Distinctually," I report. "He came with rose-bud tokens so frequently I thought that he was a florist."

"We intend to make this wedding so joyful that we are all quite miserable preparing for it," he describe. "The event will be shot off at high noon."

"Are noon on a wedding day any higher than any other noon?" I require for information.

"If you paid the bills you would think so!" he explode glubly & walk in an offward direction.

Mr Editor, you would be surprised to see how much burden that wedding was to Hon. Express Co. who brought the packages! For several entire days bundles arrove in large quantities of freight. Street in front of that house was headquarters for delivery wagons. Messengers came continually bringing Merry Christmas parcels enwrapped in paper. Hon. Samule Scott, assisted by me & family, would spend long-time each day disenwrapping those parcels and gossiping about what came. Excitement. Out would drop some golden fork or swollen pitcher marked "Happy Returns."

"Why should these be labelled 'Happy Returns'?" I negotiate.

"Because," pronounce Hon. Samule with depressed eyebrows, "they are all returns of wedding presents we sent other folks."

I stand gast at this phenomenal.

Each day for 14 complete hours that hansom Scottish home stood full of dressmakers, vacuum cleaners, dentists, milliners, reporters and other necessities of life. Hon. Samule Scott walk around looking tense like a financial crisis. Mrs. Scott were always busy. When not engaged in any other housekeeping she set down and wept some tears.

"Why you wept, Hon. Lady?" I ask to know.

"I am preparing for the wedding," she say back. "No wedding can look fashionable without a few weeps."

Each morning Hon. Gladys Scott stand up with dressmaker and report with angry rage of girlish soprano, "You make me so nervus that screaming would seem pleasant!" Yet a few moments later she meet Hon. Chas Sweetberry in parlour & report with kitten words, "O Chas, I am so happy!"

My brain feel cross-eyed to hear this duplex conversation.

Friday night Hon. Tortoni, Italian caterman, back-up horse to front lawn and dump forth sifficient camp-chairs to furnish 1 complete picnic. Hon. Chas

Sweetberry & 1 clergy man come later. They meet that Scott family, including Hon. Gladys, in parlour where they lock door and say a long ceremony, walking around & giving away several times.

When Hon. Sweetberry come outside to smoke cigaret, I say to him with banzai in my voice,

"Congratulations, Mr Sir!"

"For what?" he dib.

"For your marriage which just took place," I encroach.

"That wasn't marriage," he snork. "We was just practising."

I was confused.

*　　*　　*　　*　　*

Great date of wedding was finally there. All furniture in Hon. Parlour was fixed like pews, so all could take set-down. Mrs Scott wep some more when she seen the chairs in tiers. All that home was dressed with greenish smilax like a beautiful salad. Hon. Bridebroom arrive with silk-pipe hat over his headache. Five or six best men emerge at front door wearing Floridora clothing. Bridal-maidens came in quantities looking like they wondered who would be next. Humouristical college friends walk up carrying footware, rice & other groceries. Several hack-loads of relatives was wheeled to door.

Silence.

A clergy man encroach at side door with Rev Mr. expression.

All was prepare. Yet something was not. Hon. Samule Scott rosh up to me with quiet craze.

"Togo," he whasper, "where are Chas, the bridebroom?"

"I seen him in aunty-room off library quarrelling with his necktie," I report.

Surely yes! He was there in aunty-room trying to correct the nervus behaviour of his collar button.

"This is the happiest day of my life," report Hon. Chas when dishcovered, "How my shoes hurt me!"

More silence.

All that audience now set in parlour expectfully. Humouristical college friends pass rice-package amidst eyewinks peculiar to comedians. Several relatives appear quite affectionate.

Music emerj from piano. Hon. Bridebroom with serene collar now pop forth and stand amid flowers at end of room. 2x2 now come Bridlemaidens expensively trimmed. Hon. Bride, artistically enwrapped in original Irish curtains, nextly step forth supporting her Father, who need this attention because of his quaker knees.

"You are what you say you are?" require Hon. Clergy to Bride & Broom who now stand close by.

They agree to this.

"Has somebody here an objection to this gentleman?" ask Hon. Preach to audience.

Everybody seem careless about replying. I was going to say how I thought he was too easily peeved about his neckties, but Hon. Preach neglected to wait.

When Hon. Preach explain to Bride how she must take that man for worse & more of it, she seem to feel no alarm. He warned her about several things which I could not hear. Still she was determined to be married. So Hon. Bridebroom, who seem too entranced to remember, borrow a ring from Best Man and Miss Scott became a Mrs.

Wildly onrush of friends now ensued. Kissing heard everwheres amidst sobs & other joy. Most elderly gentlemans was most dutiful about kissing Bride.

"No one shall be permitted this salute except relatives!" holla Hon. Bridebroom appearing slightly frantic.

"Then *we* must be included," report 16 humouristic college friends. "We are fraternity brothers to you." They approach with happy mob.

Nextly come wedding brekfast. This was the most latest brekfast I ever passed food for. Also it was so innapropriate for brekfast, because wine was served instid of eggs. And the only toast which they ate was drank amidst speeches. Everytime somebody poke forth harsh word about Hon. Bridebroom it seem laughing-signal for all.

"This young man," report Uncle Henry to Hon. Bride while he rose upward, "This young man remind me dishagreeably of his Uncle Hiram which led a wild life and was sent to Congress in his old age. Be careful or he will do likewise."

The blushing Bride seem very calm. It was the Bridebroom who done nearly all the blushing.

Pretty soonly the recent Mr & Mrs Sweetberry make quick-change to railroad clothing and elope together to hack outside. While they was walking down front steps those 16 humouristic college chums suddenly give Black Hand signal.

WHOSH!!

42 gallons selected rice make cyclone upon hat-plumage of that Mrs Bride who escape with screem to carriage.

BOMB!!

12 complete carpet slippers hit Mr Bridebroom with accurate target-practice just as he was lifting his legs into that cab. More feetware mingled with rice arrive in droves and hit Hon. Carriage with angry strokes. My Samurai soul stood endwise with alarm. I should prevent this cruelty.

"O stop!" I holla, roshing forwards. "Why should you attack them young folks and drive them forth with brutality after what they has went through? Toss one more rubber boot and I shall rebuke you with my rages."

While thusly I spoke one 2nd handed ballroom slipper stroked my hair and I walk away feeling absent in my brain.

Hoping you are the same
Yours truly
Hashimura Togo.

XII
FALL CLEANING

XII FALL CLEANING

To Editor Good Housekeeping Magazine, who realise how collapsed home life looks when being cleaned.

Dear Mr:

Some folks is so clean they cause considerable untidiness everywheres they go. Such was Hon. Mrs August Moon of Salem, Mass, who is another of my bosses gone by. This lady got a house containing mahogany chairs which was brought over by Hon. Pilgrim Fathers when they was running ferryboat *Cauliflower* between Salem and Grand Rapids, Mich. She revere her furniture and all her other ancestors. Each day she require me to stroke her mahogany lovingly with furniture polish.

This Hon. Lady are very superstitious about dirt. She think it are not clean to have around. She imagine dust, soot & mildew enter her house like a burgler and Togo must be a policeman to arrest it when it gets inside.

"Togo," she say, while I am enslaving myself amidst dishwater in kitchen, "I just heard a mouse making footprints in attic. Rosh up with mop, please, and remove his muddy tracks."

I do so.

"Togo," she requesh nextly, "six autumn leaves has fell on the walk befront of the house. Gather them in your apron and burn them thoroughly in kitchen stove, taking care that no ashes escape."

I do so.

"Togo," she hypothecate, "I can observe two fly-tracks running over portrait of my ancestor, Gov. Beelzebub Biggs. Kindly to wash his face carefully with cast-steel soap and don't offend his dignitary."

This also I accomplish compressing the insurgent feeling that arise continuously in my elbows.

"The early bird obtains worms," she say cheerly when I arise at 4.32 a. m. for scrubb with sudds.

"At such time as this I prefer sleep to worms," are smart reply I make.

"To-day we shall commence housecleaning," she report last Fryday a. m.

"*Commence* it!" I communicate crossly like Napoleon. "When did we ever discontinue to houseclean?"

"Ah ho!" she laugh at. "What you has been doing is merely lick-and-promise. Housecleaning are different. To houseclean you must pull down everything that is up and pull up everything that is down. Home must be carried out into the back yard and throughly swep. All dust in house must be shoved out onto carpets which are on clothesline; then all carpets on clothesline must be brutably punished with clubs until dust fly back into house. And so on until exhausted."

I could not disobey such wise demand. So I remove off coat and commence eloping up & down stair, each time carrying some variety of pianos and mahogany dresser. My suspenders bulged with gigantic strength while Hon. Mrs Moon stood near and explained how I was more weak than Irish labour.

That house were completely filled with break-a-brack and other dishes which had been shot full of holes by mean British in Battle of Revolution which occurred in 1492. There was many plates & cups, beautiful but very lame. I drop several of these in removal, and they look more broke than usual. Several of them fell down stairs ahead of me and arrived with considerable crashes.

"I estimate my loss at $580 which must be removed from your wages," Mrs Moon say-so while she stood mourning over those fractured relicks.

I reply by saying nothing.

I rip up carpets with strength peculiar to a giant full of steam. I throw him on clothesline and trott backwards for more. I bathe Mr Moon's painted ancesters with soap-wash till they look nearly handsome. I polish floors, door, silver & hardwear with continuous rapidity. I wash stove with sudds and clean 14 pairs gloves with gasolene.

Then another breakage occur which were too bad. I was smoothing one snobbish-looking china-closet with rags, when I axidentally broke him endwise by dropping out of window. Mrs. Moon could not help from noticing.

"$19.82 extra subtracted from your wages!" she holla arithmatically.

No intelligent reply from me.

Hon. Mrs Moon spend morning in attic opening reverend trunks and fetching forth quilts & skirts belonging to Pilgrims. These I also pin to clothes-line. Nextly I brosh wall-paper with whisk and climb to roof where I save a white cat which had crolled up drain-pipe to suicide himself. I receive no extra pay for this kindness. While doing thusly I burst $27 worth of windows and bill was sent to me by Mrs Moon who holla how much it was.

I carry 6 tons complete books from cellar to library on 3rd floor. When I find they no belong there I took them back again. I also transmit considerable bags containing coal from woodshed to basement where it look more comfortable.

Very sorry event occurred when I was washing 48 eggs shell china cups. Shelf of table upturned and all splatter to floor. Mrs Moon screech and charge it to my account.

After that I paint back porch, carry sideboards, croll over all ceilings of rooms to fish away cobwebs with broom and stuff upholstery into all lounges what need it.

Mrs Moon were a very thoughtful woman. She always thought of something more for me to do with arms and legs. When I was on top-ladder dusting chandeliers she suddenly remember her mother's fire-screen she had not seen since Agnes was married.

"Go down cellar and open 11 boxes containing trash and see if mother's fire-screen ain't there."

I do so. It were not.

"Nail them up again quickly," she comment. "Then go to roof and sweep out chimbley."

I elevated myself to loftly position and stood poking smok-tracks from chimbley. Just then she holla,

"Come down 1st floor, please, and ade me in removing tables upstairs."

I do so wishing I was a bird and could fly up and down with less feetsteps.

By that time Hon. Sun were setting and I feel like doing the same. So I choose soft chair in back yard and soothe myself by flopping to it. There I reposed amidst rags, rugs, brooms, portraits, paints and other cleanly dirt.

"Why you set there so worklessly?" she require, seeing me with eagle expression.

"I have moved so much that I am now moveless," I reply with great pathos.

She make her eyes look kind and charity.

"Maybe you tired!" she collapse with considerable gentleness.

"Ah no, Mrs Madam," I contuse chivalrously. "I not tired—I merely exhausted."

"Servants should be cherished as well as masters," she say scientifically. "I acknowledge my carelessness. In enthusiasm of housecleaning I forgot you was as apt to get fatigued as any other horse. I permit you to feel weary, because you are Japanese and not strong like a Irish labour. I forgive this fault in you."

"O thank you so many for that gentle heart!" I report back, enjoying slight tear-drop from gratitude.

"No, Togo, you may rest," she say. "But while you are resting, would you please go out to back yard and beat a few Brussels carpets?"

Excuse me, Mr Editor, for acting so unobliged to a lady. But I could not do furthermore. My arms walk out on strike when I attempt to make them work. So I go to kitchen and arrive back with satchel grip and derby hat.

"Sweethearted Mrs Madam," I report, "I realise how my mind is too lightweight for your serious employment. Therefore I quit. How much you estimate I owe you for damage, breakage & crackage I done to-day?"

"1230.50 would cover everything," she suppose.

"At my present wage-pay of $5 per weekly," I snuggest, "I should be very elderly Japanese before last instalment was pay off. Therefore I shall not encumber you by waiting so long."

"But what shall I do about that bill?" she require nervely.

"Ah, Mrs Madam, you are honest lady," I bounce back. "I are sure I can trust you to keep that bill more better than anybody else."

"You done my household considerable injury," she sum up.

"I are willing to forgive that also," I repartee. "Therefore, if you will present me with 50c out of what I owe you, I shall retreat by trolley and leave your home safe from me."

She contribute 25c from purse, because she say she can't get no more change until her husband get back. That gentleman are in Arabia collecting rugs, so I decide it was too long to wait for 25c.

When nextly seen I was standing on depot-station in New England R. R. asking Hon. Ticket Merchant if he would sell me fare to some city where folks never clean house except when scolded by Brd of Health.

Hoping you are the same
Yours truly
Hashimura Togo.

- 59 -

XIII
APARTMENT HOUSE LIFE IN NEW YORK

XIII APARTMENT HOUSE LIFE IN NEW YORK

To Editor Home & Lady page whose wisdom is furniture for many apartments.

Dear Mr:

Excuse my handwriting for being cramped this time—I have been living in one N. Y. apartment-house where everything is squeezed. I tell you.

A short time of yore I seen following advertisement-news in N. Y. Paper:

> WANTED: Small-size Japanese required to do housework in fashionable apartment. Must be able to squeeze deliciously tight between furniture and to take up no room whatsoever. No fat persons required. Apply to Mrs. Buckingham Jinx, Matterhorn Apts.

I was entirely proud & nervus, Mr Editor, to apply to that jobs. Formerly I had been simple, jayseed Japanese working in ½ size towns where nothing was large. But here I was in great city of N. Y. where everything was giganterous & big. Home-life here, I thought, must be unlimited like Pennsylvania Depots.

This show how thoughtless we are when we think.

I go to address of that Jinx lady, which is at No 333 W 333rd Street, comfortable neighbourhood where 20 miles of sky-scrape homes are clumped together attempting to look quaint. I was proud to see their swollen size. How expansive it was for Japanese Schoolboy to be employed in city where everything was so big that even small cottages look like Flatiron Bldgs! Already I begin to feel pity for Peoria where folks must choke in 2 story houses.

Pretty soonly I arrive to Matterhorn Apts. How stylishly enormalous it was! I never observed a place with more upstairs. 12 complete stories I could count with my sore neck. And so fashionable to go into! Its frontside entrance was filled with marble halls, fountains, brassy electricity, golden elevators, noble niggero boys in uniform of admirals. This was most biggest entrance in America, and I was certainly sure that folks what live in those apartments upstairs must enjoy such grand-size rooms they have to ride motorcycles between parlour and dinning-room.

While thusly I thought Swedish gentleman in proud overalls arrive up.

"What you wish, standing there foolishly?" he require.

"Do you own this palace?" I ask to know.

"Yes," he report peevly. "I are the Janitor."

"I am suprised by this Matterhorn house," I explode. "The mountainous steepness of its apartments apalls me."

"The mountainous steepness of its rents would apall you more, if you seen them," he explain with insulting eyebrows.

So he poke me to elevator where I was uplifted to 9 floors. Folks living in apartment house leads very up-and-down life. When they go outside they must be elevated downwards, when they return they must be vice versa. It are impossible to see how folks can be level in such home life, and yet it is.

Hon. Mrs Jinx, entirely Duchess appearing lady, meet me at doorway with Vanderbilt nose.

"This are my apartment," she express, pointing to a hallway surrounded by expensive looking cells filled with gilty furniture, pianolas, painted portraits, rugs and mahoganish tables resembling J. P. Morgan.

"Yes," I report. "This are your apartment—but where is your home?"

"In N. Y.," she report with Waldorf expression, "home is where we pay our rent."

Mr Editor, when that lady show me her apartment I was jigged by surprise. Each room was less than life-size, yet it contain wealth resembling Buckingham. Mahoganish doors, plush walls, luxury here and there—but where was there room to live in?

"This are drawing-room," she indicate, making points to Pullman-car compartment containing gas-log and French-speaking furniture. I should like to set down in such a room, but the chairs was in the way.

She show me dinning-room. It contain four-plate-power table, portraits of fish on walls and shelf with several beery steins with German motto, "Drinken, Dranken, Drunken."

"This cozy room are good for small banquets," she acknowledge.

"Small banquets is oftenly the most limited," I encouridge.

She show me library.

"This are called the snuggery," she condole. I felt very congested to look at it. Folks must snug very snugly to snuggle into such a snuggery. On high top shelf was following books to show it was a library: "Pilgrum's Progress," "Life of John Drew," "Bradstreet on Financial Failures," "Blue Book of N. Y. Smarty Set."

Under table was poker chips to entertain scholars while reading.

Nextly she show me kitchen. O shocks! It were size like the interior of a upright piano. Hon. Gas Stove look chilly from setting too close to Hon. Ice Box which was hot from contax with gas stove.

"This Kitchen are small but comfortless," she explain braskly. "It are slightly compressed, yet there is room for everything to cook with."

"One thing to cook with there is no room for," I snuggest.

"What should that be?" she require.

"The cook," I explain.

"Smallish Japanese is capable of squeezing," she fire back.

Nextly she ope door by Kitchen and show me one dark-complexioned cubby hole to look at.

"What a nice vegetable closet!" I report. "But too small, perhaps, for large cabbages."

"That are not a vegetable closet—it are a servant's bedroom," she develop.

I would be astonished, but there was no room.

Sardines gets used to living in cans, Mr Editor; so I soonly became acquainted with how to live in N. Y. flat without knock-off of elbow. It were umpossible to turn around in all rooms, but I could get out of doors by backing up.

This Mrs Jinx got a husband who are a broker, but not yet broke. He come home nights long enough to change clothes and take his wife to some other Roof Garden. For conversation he complain of his debts.

"Why should we live in flat we can't afford?" he jowl, reaching across dinning-room to get a match.

"Mr Husband!" report Hon. Mrs with spasma, "how could you forget to remember our position? In this house live 2 families intimately acquainted with a Trust. Also, look at our main entrance downstairs—it are a bigger waiting room than the Grand Central Station and twice as lonesome. This house got the brightest buttons, swiftest elevator and crosset janitor in New York."

Sometime Mrs Jinx have company for dinner. Her dinning-room was sifficient for 4. Therefore she ask 10. N. Y. folks is conveniently compressible, especially when fat. Folks wearing diamonds in front of them would arrive to these dinners and explain why they wasn't at Newport.

"How nicely you are situated here," they snuggest, looking sidewise.

"O surely yes!" obligate Hon. Mrs. "We have splandid view of the airshaft from library window and our dinning-room overlook some of the finest advertising signs in the city."

"So fortunate you are with so much room!" say lady wearing diamond bib on chest. "In our apartment we are pusitively crowded."

No one could believe it.

"Why do you keep a canary?" ask one gentleman of one lady.

"Because I have no room for a parrot," say one lady to one gentleman.

And so onward.

My cookery is deliciously abominable, thank you, in that 1-8 size kitchen. Yet those N. Y. persons is so refined they can disguise any taste by politeness.

"You have a chef, I suspect?" require one brokerish gentleman gnawing my chicken crokets.

"Two of them," deceive Mrs Jinx with 5th Ave expression. I arrive to room looking proud with dishes. "This Togo are my faithful butler inherited from my grandfather who was a lawyer and kept many retainers."

I am alarmed to hear such large conversation in such small space. And yet I acted very intelligent, considering my stupidity.

My life in that compartment become more and more homeless as time relapsed. Hon. Mrs Jinx were the most stay-away lady I ever seen. She say she go out to get the air; and I could not blame her. For 2 entire weeks she was somewheres else all time. In early a. m. after 10 o'clock she go down town for get hats, manicure & other jewelry. By noon she telephone, "I shall not be home lunch, because I am too busy wasting time with Mrs Swatts-Byng." By night she telephone, "I shall not be home dinner, because I am taking my Husband to eat at Astoria hotel, afterwards we shall go see musical-comical theater."

Lonesomeness arrived to me as much as that apartment would hold. It were true I could breathe more with less persons taking up room; yet my thoughts became all by themselves. I feel like Hon. Robinson Caruso on a vacant island.

One early a. m. Hon. Mrs uprose for breakfast early at 11 o'clock. She approach to me with tear-drop eye.

"Togo," she say, "you have been with me 5 entire weeks. Therefore you can be considered the oldest family servant in N. Y. I shall reward you with bad news. My Husband has did so much brokerage in Wall Street that he has broke. Therefore, we shall be more tight compressed than usual."

"How could it?" I ask feelishly.

"We must move to a smaller flat," she glub. "Will you faithfully follow us thereto?"

"Mrs Madam," I entrench, "I might do faithfully what you say. I might follow you to smaller flat, but how could I squeeze in when I got there? Excuse me while I go to Arizona where I can stand with 1000 miles on each side of me and can turn over in bed without wounding my elbows on a washstand. Indians does not live so high as New Yorkers, but they lives much broader."

Hon. Mrs explode her voice from my words and attemp' to imprison my escape by locking front door. But she could not. With Samurai war-cry I open umbruella and, attaching myself to handle, I make jump-out from bedroom window and flew 9 stories like Hon. Glen Curtiss.

When I arrived to pave-walk Hon. Janitor see me and report,

"You are broken out with lunacy."

Hoping you are the same,
Yours truly,
Hashimura Togo.

XIV
CAN AUTOMOBILES BE TAMED FOR HOME USE?

XIV CAN AUTOMOBILES BE TAMED FOR HOME USE?

To Editor Home and Lady Page who are so smooth of heart and soft of mind he can safely introduce gasolene into most explosive families.

Dear Hon. Mr!—With delicious rapidity I shot off from my last situation of work, care Mrs. Seth Hopp, Camden, N. J. This lady admire my talent so much she appoint me to every task of a disagreeable nature. In her supply of housework she include one slight, grey ottomobile of one-lung capacity and asthma of engine. This machinery are like mosquitos, small but cross.

Mr. Editor, I have always dreaded to get acquainted with ottomobiles because they are connected with so many crimes. Yet when I am employed as Gen. Houseworker in a house where a cook must understand chauffering, what could I?

Last Munday a. m. Hon. Mrs. Hopp approach to me with racetrack expression and corrode,

"Togo, as soonly as you finish washing dishes, go out to garage and wash ottomobile. Then take him down to R R depot to meet Mr. Hopp at 5.66 train."

"I do not understood your ottomobile," I abject.

"Nobody does," she say cheerly. "Yet I are sure you can become mister of this difficult wagon, because Japanese are extra bright little people."

I thank her with bent stomach. And yet calm nervousness straddled my heart.

As soonly as I had finished bathing dishes, Hon. Mrs. lead me forthly to gas-stable where that iron animal stood amidst awful perfumery. I was shocked to observe the cruel expression of lamps with which he gazed at me.

"He are simple and good natured when you know his habits," she explain.

"This truth are also true of vampires," I dib for frights.

"Your duty must be to dust him night and morning, manicure his carborette and train him to obey. When you learn to control him, it shall be your duty to drive Hon. Mr. Hopp back & forthly. I show you how to learn."

Hon. Mrs go to home & put on racetrack hat peculiar to motor. Then she teach me free lesson.

Firstly she go to front nose of Hon. Ottomobile and twist crank resembling ice-cream freezer. Mad trembly arrive from his insides!

"Now he are ready to do anything," collapse Hon. Mrs dragging me to seat besides her. I set here holding on to my soul.

"Observe my antics if possible," she commit with extreme dexterity of thumbs, heels, hands & elbows while she poke 6 buttons, jerk 1 doz handles, inflame electricity and make goose-cry by horn.

I sat gast to see her. WHOOSH!! We commence onward.

"That are way to start ottomobile," holla Mrs Seth Hopp while avoiding death on road & wheeling corners with aviator expression.

"It are easy like astronomy," I rejoint, holding on to my hair to keep him from blowing off. And so forth.

At R. R. station we stop up and load on Hon. Mr. Hopp, one large, portable man of important fat.

"Togo are learning to chaff this car so he can drag you back & forth," decry Hon. Mrs.

"He do not look very powerful," contuse him cattishly.

How could he realise?

Mr. Editor, driving ottomobiles are a warlike work unsuited to Gen. Housekeeping. How can I do hired girl tasks, yet expect myself to command those harsh cranks and greasy energy what makes gasolene go? To make a chauffeur out of a cook are like making bullets out of buscuits. It could be done, but can it?

Yet this Mrs. Seth Hopp, Hon. Lady of extreme brain, was determined I should be a chum to her car, although I were sure he did not like my looks. Each morning for ½-hour time she give me lesson in how to start ottomobiles. I learn this with all the fido qualities of my Japanese religion. Yet something told me different.

"This horsepower are full of mules," I tell her one day while I set there pulling 13 handles expecting Hon. Car to go when he would not.

"Brace uply!" she say for courage. "Any child can start an ottomobile."

"Why you not employ a child, then?" I require.

I could see by her silence that she did not admire my rudeness.

After practice I become more intellectual with that machinery. With kindly assistance from Hon. Mrs I could tease him to start from his barn and run dangerously around block amid loudy curses from gasolene. Pride filled me up. Folks often feels thusly before cyclones.

That p. m. Hon. Mrs arrive to kitchen where I was manufacturing pie with mushroom expression peculiar to cooks.

"Togo," she denounce, "you sippose you can now start Hon. Ottomobile by your lonesome self?"

"No starter could ever be more scientific than me," I negotiate, holding pie-crust on my wrists.

"Glad to hear!" she congratulate. "Hon. Mr. Hopp return to-night by 6.6½ train. Feed 2 gals gasolene to Hon. Ottomobile and deliver Hon. Husband to me as soonly as possible."

This were supreme time for prides. Bellboys, admirals and postmasters seldom feel more happy in time of great victory.

I put on respectaful gloves & greasy overcoat to resemble chauffer. I smudge some engine-smoke across nose, so I should look more mechanical. Then I go to gas-stable and quell Hon. Ottomobile with my hero expression. He seem quite doggish.

Skilful cranks by me. Loud roary from his stomach. Like Hon. Julius Cæsar crossing the Delaware I lep to seat & make my heels, thumbs & elbows go in all directions. O banzai! That sweet, tame ottomobile jump forwards like a canary. Defly I turn wheel and make him sidle up one street & down next. Citizens was seen dodging respectfully side by side to let me pass. One gentleman raise Bull Moose voice and mention it when I scratch his knuckles slightly. More faster and yet more so I sped onwards. I seem to be walking on golden wings. Poetry circulated in my chest. Thusly do gasolene make heroes of us all.

Pretty soonly I arrive up to R R station where I observe Hon. Hopp standing there in all the importance of his fat. Him & several conductors looked very gast when they observe great skill with which I knocked hitching-post from befront of saloon and still came on.

All wheels was waltzing nicely as I turn Hon. Car close to platform, intending for to stop and load on Hon. Boss.

But alast! when I got there I could not stay. Despite of how I wiggled handles, punched buttons, reversed myself with heels and commanded with voice, that inflamed chariot were deaf to pity and determined to continue onward. Hon. Mr make motions for me to arrest myself, but all I could do was to set in seat while Hon. Car gollup rudely around block. With Samurai calmness I continue to turn wheel, hoping thusly to arrive back to station. And so I did. Pretty soonly I come up to R R platform again. Despite my angry jerks by handle, I could observe how peevly Hon. Hopp look at me.

"Togo," he holla, "come here!"

"I do so!" I response, so I make skilled wobble of wheel and drove Hon. Ottomobile up on platform, where he go for Hon. Boss so straight that this fatty gentleman start off with dodge run peculiar to ducks avoiding elephants. But Hon. Ottomobile was more quicker in the legs, so he pounce on Hon. Mr with rude affection peculiar to New Foundland dogs. Groans by him. Toots by otto. Then onwards I proceeded, still attempting to strangle that horsepower which would not quit.

Mr. Editor, you could not imagine such stubborn bullishness could be in anything not human. The more I twisted that wagon, the faster he go. Ditches, back fences and trees were splintered by his determination. At lastly, because I knew it would be convenient for me to die near the place where I was employed, I turned his nose toward home of Hon. Mrs Hopp.

We got there by very cross lots. Mrs. Hopp were standing by front gate when I whoofed by.

"Togo," she yall as I pass, "Did you get my husband?"

"Yes, thanks—I got him plenty," were smart reply I make.

Pretty soonly, by intense wheeling, I come back around block to where that sweet-hearted lady was.

"Put that car back in its stable!" she shreech like eagles.

"I obey!" was reply for me. So with all the Japanese courage I could demand from my ancestors, I turn Hon. Car through front fence, over vegetable garden, across clothes line. When I arrive to garage I put Hon. Car in very neatly, but Hon. Garage refuse to remain standing where he was, but followed in several fractions. 26 feet further on, Hon. Ottomobile, cursing like enraged kangaroos, lep over that cyclone and fall dead in heap of splinters. Nothing alive remained except a few wheels, pandemonium and me.

As soonly as my intellectual mind got back in place, I sat up, determined to see Hon. Mrs about resigning from that dangerous housework. But she saw me previously.

"Togo!" she glub, "how dares you make this rumpage when I spend one whole week teaching you how to start ottomobiles?"

"If you had spent another week teaching me how to stop him, I should be less scattered," were bright reply from me.

So I remove my derby from around my neck & limp offwards feeling like tonsilitis.

Hoping you are the same
Yours truly,
Hashimura Togo.

XV
A PICNIC PARTY

XV A PICNIC PARTY

To Editor Home & Lady Page who enjoys fresh air best when slightly cooked:

Hon. Dear Sir:—

Why should tame folks wish to be wild when they are getting along in nice candition without any Nature around? I ask to know. Hon. Mrs Horse W. Snow, by who I was discharged away recently, might still nourish me in her house if it was not for fresh air subject I tell you about:

This Hon. Snow family reside in Trenton, N. J., where they live. Hon. Mrs Snow have got two (2) complete twins, Frederick & Ederick, age 4 yrs. old each. Hon. Horse W. Snow have got asthma. So every one enjoys affliction in his own way.

Last Fryday, when I was in Hon. Kitchen manufacturing pies by baking it, Hon. Mrs approach up to me & explan,

"Togo," she say it, "do you unstand picnics?"

"What kind of Gen. Housekeeping are that?" I ask to enquire.

"It are the only kind what can be did outdoors," she report.

"How do you make a picnic?" are next question for me.

"Picnics can be manufactured by following recipee," she snuggest:

> "1st:—Fill an ottomobile with children, pie & other sandwitches;
>
> 2st:—Find a piece of Nature and set down on it with lunch;
>
> 3st:—Continue this programme until go-home time, then do so."

I listened with wrapped attention.

"Cannot Nature be seen without taking lunch along?" I ask off.

"I have no time to answer statistics," she dib hashly. "To-morrow morning by early a. m. we depart away in ottomobile for find some soft place in Nature to sit on. I wish you prepare lunch of delicious hard-boiledness to include egg, chicken, more eggs, cake, some eggs, sandwitches & confused varieties of pie."

"I obey similar to soldiers," in voice from me.

"And don't forget the eggs," she reproach while eloping away.

That ottomobile of Hon. Horse W. Snow are a 7 passenger car. Therefore it do not act surprised when 10 persons of sorted sizes gets into it. Thusly, it look last Satday morning by early a. m. when Hon. Ottomobile give hoots similar to martyrs about to enjoy break down. Included among those getting in was Mrs & Mr Horse W. Snow & 2 twins; Mr & Mrs Hamlet J. Dilk & 2 yrs. old Arthur; Togo & food; Ethel & Albert, lovely young folks who look at each other with fiancee expression.

Honks by Hon. Otto.

Hon. Horse W. Snow, who was at the wheel pushing gasolene, say, "I have look forwards to this day for joyful time."

"We shall have delightful picnic," renig Mrs Horse W. "Togo, why are you so unintellectual as to carry pie with its head downwards?"

"This are delightful day to find Nature at home," say Hon. Horse W. with happy smiling.

"It are," derange Hon. Mrs. "Horse, why you insist on wheeling through so many bumps that my elbows shake loose?"

"Let us go to Buttermilk Falls where moss is there," snuggest Hon. Dilk.

"Buttermilk Falls are full of disgust," report Hon. Mrs Dilk.

They would doubtlessly enjoyed some more quarrel, but they were discontinued by rumpage in their midst where Hons. Ederick & Frederick was making slaps to Hon. Dilk baby, age 2. Weeps.

Everybody wish go somewhere else. Ethel wish go Lover's Leap. Albert require go Altoona Vista. Hon. Mrs Snow demand go Trolley View Park. I wish go home, but everybody was careless to ask my requirements.

But Hon. Snow, who was driving ottomobile, took us to Morning Glory Glenn, because nobody wish go there.

Morning Glory Glenn were nice landscape resembling some photos of Nature I have seen. It include wooden trees, a wet brook, considerable wasps & other outdoor symptoms.

"Togo," say Hon. Snow with boss expression, "I shall attend to all the hard work of this picnic if you fetch 8 buckets water, cut down 11 trees, make Dutch oven by piling stones, put baby to sleep, watch twins and bake potatus."

"This are very restful spot," report Hon. Ethel.

I did not notice it. Nature look like any other kitchen to me, except there was more room to get tired in.

In the immediate meanwhile all that picnic were unfastening lunching basket and enjoying many unpleasant things about him.

"Who spilled mustard in angel cake?" require Hon. Snow looking like a jury.

"Togo," report Hon. Mrs Snow peevly.

I say nothing by chopping wood.

"Who broke 17 eggs & forgot to bring butter while doing so?" approach Hon. Ethel with finacee eyebrows.

"Togo," snuggest Hon. Albert with engaged expression.

I carry silent firewood to blazes.

Hon. Mrs Dilk spread down tablecloth of Turkish redness & make him look good housekeeping by putting plates, pickles, ham & saucers on him.

"It are going to rain!" report all together like chorus girls.

"I are to blame for that also," I acknowledge.

All seem pleased to hear my crime, yet no intellectual reply.

By wet water of runnybrook, Frederick & Ederick was playing Indian by using Mrs Dilk's 2 yrs. old baby for a prisoner. Pretty soonly, they dropped Hon. Baby in wet water to see how well he float. He did not do so, thank you; therefore I must plunge myself in and remove Baby out. He notice my chivalry by angry howells.

"I have saved your Baby from a watery tombstone," I report to Mrs Dilk.

"Could you not save him without wetting his feet so seriously?" she ask out crankerously.

"Next time he drowns, he should carry an umberella!" I snuggest, while poking potatus in fire where they would burn better.

Hon. Sky now look very sorry like he expect rain. Yet not yet. Lunching were nearly most prepared. Ethel & Albert were enjoying disagreeable love-talk,

Hon. Snow & Hon. Dilk was drinking appetite from bottel, Frederick & Ederick was weeping as usual—when Oh!!!! Hon. Mrs Dilk come hop-jump over hill and make following explanation:

"Bull! Bull!!"

We could hear somebody talking moo-language slightly off in distance.

"Who shall save us?" require Hon. Snow, picking up Ed. & Fred. (twins) while Hon. Mrs Dilk obtained Baby.

Looking over the eyebrow of the hill, I observe one fatherly cow enjoying salad of daisy-cup blossoms. He seemed to be a smiling cattle of Tammany Hall nature.

"Togo," require Hon. Snow with militia expression, "you go scare Hon. Bull offwards while me & Mr Dilk bravely save wives & children."

They all began walking backwards to fence 86 feet away. That Hon. Bull appear very civilized, so I was sure he would go away by request. I had read in news-print, somewheres, that bulls are afraid of red rags; therefore, I took up that reddy tablecloth and approach close by his nose making waves with it.

"Shoo!" I repeat like a toreador.

All folks, while running, yell, "Don't do! Don't do!" but I was too busy scaring bulls to make notice of them.

All suddenly, Hon. Bull look upwards & observe my antix. He must of been extra brave, because that red rag did not scare him slightly. Snores of rage from him. He begin pawing grass with finger-nails. Loudly bellus by him. Then—O rush!! He elevated his horns downwards and make gollup for me.

When I see how ambitious he look, I did one great heroism: I continued to wave red rag & rush towards them picnic folks so I could be there to protect them when Hon. Bull begin to hook. They was 48 feet ahead of me, but me & Hon. Bull run very fast. I keep ahead, because he stop to swear two or three times. We reached Hon. Fence together, just as Hon. Snow & Hon. Dilk was getting over with armful of family.

Roars!! That grand-square animal kicked me with horns so skilfully that I made airship movement & come down on fence just in time to help Hon. Dilk & family fall over. Yet they was thankless. Everybody was on other side by that time. You would think they should be happy to see me light among them—yet not.

Hon. Bull spent 36 minutes making angry promenades up & down fence talking oratory in cow language. Then he go back to where Hon. Lunch was & spent rest of afternoon kicking it into river with horns.

Hon. Sky begin to rain & them (2) twins made it wetter by weeps. All wish to go homewards, but that was umpossible, because Hon. Ottomobile were in field next to where Hon. Bull were setting down.

At 7:26 p. m. time, Hon. Farmer come along with moustache under chin & offer to coax off Bull, price $5.

"He are harmless," interrogate Hon. Farmer.

"I know it," report Hon. Snow. "He merely chased us to tell us so."

We all got into car, pretty soonly, and start homewards amidst considerable drips and shipwrecked feelings of stumach.

"Shakspeare never wrote nothing so tragic like to-day," glub Hon. Snow.

"Dearie, when you see Nature, you must take him like he comes," snuggest Hon. Mrs.

"He'll have to come to my house, next time I see him," he dib.

When we arrive up to R. R. station, I was surprised: Hon. Snow stop ottomobile.

"Togo," he say so, "This are where you get off."

"You wish me depart homeless?" I snagger.

"Since you are so smart at flagging bulls," he resnort, "maybe you can wave red rags at engineer and tell him take you some place where picnics is unknown & brains unnecessary."

Speaking thusly, Hon. Ottomobile depart away full of honks.

Hoping you are the same,
Yours truly,
Hashimura Togo.

XVI
AN ADVENTURE IN BANTING

XVI AN ADVENTURE IN BANTING

To Editor Ladies' Page which are never too fat to seem agreeable.

Hon Mr: Last job I were divorced from were home of Hon. Mrs Violet J. Bobb who resides in the suburbs of Illinois. This Hon. Bobb lady seem very wholsale about her beauty which contain 207 lbs complete poise.

One day she approach to me & report,

"Togo," she say so, "I am going to have a reduction of myself."

"Will you be a great bargain?" I ask to know.

"Ah surely yes!" she deploy. "I intend to be marked down from 207 lbs to 180 in one month."

I show my amazement by surprise.

"What will Hon. Mr Bobb say," I rebuke, "when he return to dinner each p. m. and find his Love growing less and less? Would you shrink thusly from the hand that feeds you?"

"If that hand did not feed me so much, perhapsly I would be less mountainous," she gollup.

Yet she were determined. With immediate quickness she send to Hon. Dr Physician and get Aunty Fat cure. Following was recipe for it:

1st—Make things disagreeable for self and others.

2st—Dress in rubber shirt-waist & exercise until entirely unhappy. Keep on doing so.

3st—Avoid sleep by keeping awake.

4st—Avoid foods in any form. Beef tea & hard tack may be used as a substitute. Add Gen. Discomfort.

5st—Keep away from pleasant thoughts, as these are very fatty.

6st—Shun all proteids, caryatids and asteroids.

Mr Editor, did you ever try to cook for a lady what requires nothing to eat but hard tack & beef tea? Such work might be easy, but it ain't. Supplying her with meals were like feeding canned vacuum to camels—light work, but deliciously scientific.

Hon. Mr Bobb, who was thin and red headed like a match, could eat a banquet multiplied by three each day and appear just as wirey as before. Foods make him thinner, so he require it continuously. Therefore, I must cook very lopsided meals for them Bobbs to eat it. For dinner-eat Hon. Bobbs absorb veal stew containing potatus, fricaseed gravy, hot buns & beans of great wealth. But Hon. Mrs Bobbs give me strick orders to serve her only bowl of soupless broth with plate of very hard tack.

"I appreciate bravery of soldiers," she say, eating with gnaws.

"Why should it?" reply her husband.

"Because," she wep, "after eating hard tack for 1 week I should be willing to die for Country or anything else."

For dessert Hon. Mr had a minced pie while Hon. Mrs had a hysteric. When Hon. Mr seen this noise he run to telephone and report.

"Oh Dr, Dr!" he holla, "Hon. Mrs have got one hysteric!"

"So glad to hear!" rejoint Hon. Medicine with smiling voice. "Grief are a great reducer."

Hon. Mrs took walking exercise every morning from 9 o'clock until she got back. In this promenade she resemble elephants marching in Siamese funeral—each footstep seemed to go in front of the other with sorry expression of great weight. When she return back she set down in parlour attempting to deceive herself into staying awake.

"Your lunching are prepared on table," I pronounce with servant voice.

"Please do not call beef tea lunching!" she snib like a cross stork.

She set down and et hard tack with extreme desolation.

After lunching she go groanfully to upstairs side. Pretty soonly I hear plaster and other brick-a-brack falling amidst considerable earthquake, so I know Hon. Mrs was rolling her figure over the carpet.

After 2 complete weeks of this hygiene had went by, Hon. Bobbs come home one night with scales for weighing coal.

"Now we shall observe how much you have subtracted by efforts," he negotiate cheerly.

"I am so wasted away I can scarcely jump," she mone. She step to scales which throw up their arms with loudy clatter when she got on.

Hon. Bobbs hang considerable 100 lbs of iron to Hon. Scales before he could strike a balance. At lastly Mrs Madam was weighed.

"Dearie," report Hon. Husband with voice, "You have not suffered all for vain. You have lost exactly ½ lb!"

She fainted all over him.

Mr. Editor, there are nothing more injurious to life than doing what is good for us. Folks seeking health are considerable insurance risk. Dutiful persons is nearly always cross, and dypsepia are the favourits pastime of folks what never do no harm to their interior stomachs.

Me & Hon. Bobbs got entirely worried about how Hon. Mrs was making behaviour. In losing 2 lbs she dropped her spirits 1 ton. So I make lecture to her on this subjeck one day.

"Why you live in midst of groceries & take nothing?" I ask out. "Sailors enjoys more bill of fare when shipwrecked on logs. When driven desperado by hunger thay can at leastly cook each other."

"Not having to drink beef tea are sifficient to make them happy," she croke with Ibsen voice.

All day she behave with air of rejected alimony. When her Husband encroach home by night time he notice this.

"Kitten," he require, "how much pounds you lost to-day?"

Peeved silence by her.

"O dearie," he deplore. "If you continue this bant some longer, home will never seem snug again. Since you started to reduce, you have become fatter and me thinner. In attempting to reduce your waist you merely make your mind narrow. The less you eat the more biting your replies becomes. O fill my home like once you used to do, or I shall blow off and become suddenly zero!"

Thus he say it with voice like a sad actor. But she merely set exercising her elbows cruely like a Svoboda.

Next morning while Hon. Mrs were off making lonesome walk for thinness, I was in kitchen thinking thoughtfully about Fat. Why should ladies abhor this delicious padding? I ask to know. Are not round circles more beautiful than straight strings? Are not pillows more lovely as snakes? Answer is, Yes!!!

Therefore, I must lead this Boss Lady away from her emaciated mania before her husband removed himself from her peeved disposition and happy home was shipwrecked around my kitchen.

So I lit gas stove, took out recipe book, flour, sugar, apples & other nourishments and with immediate quickness I began stewing things what smelled like a banquet.

At noon time Hon. Mrs Madam come to table and set down, as usual, with forceable-feeding expression.

I put Hon. Soup befront of her. She startle.

"What food is this which smell so disobediently fragrant?" she ask out.

"Tometoes soup six inches thick & full of fatty nourishment," I rake off.

"I refuse to eat such!" she yellup—and before I could took it away she had assimilated it entirely with spoon.

Next dish were turkey hash escorted by fried potatus, cinnamoney rolls, jelly & baked bean.

"I shall scold you!" she commence, but could not do so because she was too busy forking that food with considerable smacks.

And so onward through complete programme of vegetables until she reach apple dumpling & 2 cups chocolate.

She sigh.

Pretty soonly I observe her in parlour-room laying on sofa, eating candy-box and reading Mrs Humpley Ward book for sentimental joys. Sleep arrived nextly, and I felt quite patriotic to think how peaceful she was for 2 complete hours.

At hour of 4:27 p. m. she came to kitchen with new expression of brightly smiling.

"Togo," she report, "you have saved my life by your disobedience. How dare you?"

"A Samurai ain't afraid of nothing, not even Fat," I snuggest.

"You have went strickly against my orders," she guggle. "It were a delicious meal. Yet I must punish you for your impertinence. How much wages I owe you?"

"$5," I acknowledge.

"Here are $15," she explode. "$5 for your disobedience & $10 for your talents. Henceforward you are fired."

"I was never more affectionately discharged in all my experience," I absolve while putting on hat & coat. "While I am vacant from this job would you please hire my Cousin Nogi, who is also intelligent?"

"If he are a good cook, send him around," she greet while I depart feeling like my brain was on backwards.

Hoping you are the same
Yours truly
Hashimura Togo.

Milton Keynes UK ·
Ingram Content Group UK Ltd.
UKHW010706240424
441619UK00004B/312